Fatos Lubonia

CW00740215

Fatos Lubonja
Like a Prisoner

*Translated
from the Albanian
by* **JOHN HODGSON**

First published in 2022
by Istros Books
London, United Kingdom
www.istrosbooks.com

© Fatos Lubonja 2022
First published as *Jetë Burgu* Skanderbeg Books, Tirana, 2021
Translation © John Hodgson

Cover photo: Fatos Lubonja
Typesetting: pikavejica.com

ISBN: 978-1-912545-85-8

This book has been selected to receive financial assistance from English PEN's
"PEN Translates!" programme, supported by Arts Council England. English
PEN exists to promote literature and our understanding of it, to uphold
writers' freedoms around the world, to campaign against the persecution and
imprisonment of writers for stating their views, and to promote the friendly
co-operation of writers and the free exchange of ideas. www.englishpen.org

Supported using public funding by

ARTS COUNCIL
ENGLAND

Contents

The Caged Wolf

The sight of that repellent human whirlpool has remained my only clear memory of that first day. I've forgotten most of the prisoners with whom I travelled in the dark metal box of the prison van from Tirana. I've forgotten the name of the man whose wrist was locked to mine in a single pair of handcuffs for the journey. I've forgotten almost all our conversation along the way. I remember nothing of the search we were subjected to when we climbed out of the van and stepped on the inch-thick frozen snow. But the sight before me on that chill, frosty day in February 1975, when I looked down at the prisoners' zone from the top of a flight of steps, has remained vivid in my mind as one of the most important encounters in life.

What I saw was the area I later learned that prisoners called the 'field', where I found myself staring at a strange mass of human creatures, of a kind that I had never seen in my life. I had seen larger crowds in queues, or at the gates of stadiums, but it was the way these people moved that made this swarm of humanity so unusual.

I gradually realised that what made this scene so out-landish was the way the prisoners anxiously paced to and fro, back and forth within that confined space. Whether they walked alone or in twos and threes, they all displayed the same nervous agitation, as if trying not to be sucked into a whirlpool, but unable to break free of its centripetal force. Alone in my cell, I had felt the neurotic frustration of a wolf in a cage. This was the same thing, at a collective level.

Only a few days before my arrest, I had seen on television a documentary film about the mental stress suffered by wild animals in European zoos. The most sensitive survived the journey from Africa only with great difficulty. Some like the giraffes died on the way, and others showed symptoms of different illnesses caused by their severe problems of adaptation.

I remembered the wolves best. The film showed a wolf in a cage at the zoo, endlessly pacing around in a narrow circle behind the bars, never looking outside. This animal, whose extraordinary energy enabled it to cover up to two hundred kilometres a day in the wild, was now reduced to blind, directionless circling. This endless round was a sign of neurosis. Then there were scenes of wolves in modern zoos, which had attempted to create conditions as close to nature as possible. Here the wolves felt they were merely in a larger cage, and still wandered round and round, but in a larger circle.

I would have forgotten this film, except that a few days later I was the caged wolf myself. When the guards threw me into the twilit cell for the first time and closed the door, I fell flat on my face. I lay on the floor for a few moments, or maybe hours, I have no way of telling. These were the most terrible moments of my life. Then I instinctively rose to my feet and started to pace my cell. The next morning, I started the same endless pacing once more, and again the day after. All day I crossed back and forth between the door and the opposite wall, just like the wolf in its cage.

Now, having been moved to the labour camp of Spaç, I was faced with a 'modern zoo' with more space, but still surrounded by barbed wire. That dreadful eddying crowd on the field was driven by the same neurosis as the wolves, and there was an entire pack of them. This seething humanity was given an even more remarkable appearance by the colour of the prisoners' clothes. The prevailing hue was the grey of the outworn military greatcoats that were sent to the prison storehouses and dyed with varying drab shades. But beyond those different shades of grey, these disarmed soldiers without belts or weapons were rendered even more grotesque by their hats and caps. These caps were not part of the prison uniform, but made by the prisoners themselves. They came in assorted shapes, and even a single cap would have several colours. Most were knitted from multicoloured wool or sewn from all sorts of scraps. Some could scarcely be called caps, but were mere rags pieced together to shield the head from the cold, and barely covering one ear, creating an even more repulsive appearance.

This human swarm became even uglier when it suddenly stopped its movement the moment we appeared at the top of the steps. The prisoners paused in their pacing and stared up in wide-eyed excitement at the arrival of something to brighten their lives – I later learned that in prison slang the arrival of the prison van meant a delivery of 'meat', because some of the prisoners saw in the newly-arrived young men a chance to satisfy their sexual appetites.

I felt I was entering a madhouse.

The guard who was our escort ordered us to follow him straight to the showers. The camp storekeeper, an elderly prisoner, tall and wizened, gave us the prison uniform to replace our own clothes worn in our free life. This uniform consisted of two pairs of long underwear and a shirt of tough prickly cotton that tore the skin at first, a brown duck suit, padded trousers and jacket of a colourless brown to protect us from the cold winter of Spaç, moccasins made of car tyres, and an old military greatcoat, dyed grey.

Mirrors were not allowed in the camp, so when I was taken to a room and shown where I was to sleep, I satisfied my need to see how I looked in these clothes by going to the window. I saw myself in prison uniform for the first time with mixed feelings. On one hand, here was a figure so hideously dressed that I couldn't believe it was myself, and at the same time, with freezing hands, I tried to adjust these new clothes so they would fit me as well as possible.

With this contradictory desire to adapt, and yet never to adapt, I descended the steps from the dormitory to launch myself at last into the swirling currents of my fellow-prisoners. As they welcomed me, their handshakes, the look in their eyes, their conversation, and their smiles made me realise that these creatures in their ugly caps, greatcoats and moccasins were human beings, very similar to myself and the people I had known outside. Yet I could never shake off that feeling prompted by my first sight of them, when the place had looked like a madhouse, and the sense that I had plunged into a whirlpool of people, united by the neurosis of the caged wolf, and into an existence that was a negation of everything I had lived for.

Eqerem

I

The rooftop was the largest open space in the camp. The prisoners assembled there twice a day for roll-calls and three times, at the start of each shift, to wait for the squad of duty guards that escorted us to the mine. Its surface, the size of two or three volleyball courts, was spread with concrete and enclosed by iron railings. The roof covered the baths, latrines, the store for our work-clothes, and the private kitchen. Below it stretched the perimeter fence, with its watchtowers, and then a slope that fell ever more steeply down to the stream. Opposite, above the stream, rose a range of high hills covered with scrub, climbing ever higher towards the towering peak of Munelle. This range of hills was the only landscape visible from the camp that was not ringed with wire and watchtowers. It was a tall, natural wall that blocked the horizon from the north-west to the north-east, and the prisoners gazed every day at its grim sameness and ponderous bulk. Only three isolated houses were visible on this hillside, very far apart, from which several shepherds' tracks descended, appearing and disappearing through the scrub and bracken. These paths met below at the bridge over the stream, which lay as far as our eyes could see from the rooftop.

It was only during the morning wait on the rooftop that the monotony of the landscape was broken for a few moments, when a young girl who lived in one of the three houses would climb down the slope. Her descent, from the moment she appeared until she reached the bridge over the stream and vanished from sight, took some time.

People said she worked in the mine administration. Someone had given her the nickname 'the Doe', and that is what everybody called her. Occasionally, some women of Mirdita in their local costume would appear on the hillside opposite, but not even the prisoners' ravenous sexual stare could penetrate their trousers, wrapped around with skirts. The Doe was the only woman ever to appear on that hillside dressed simply in trousers that emphasised her fine, round thighs, with muscles that swelled as she leaned her weight on the stony steps of the path.

The prisoners on the rooftop could see her as soon as she emerged from her house, which was a long way off. At first, she was a barely distinguishable smudge among the rocks and undergrowth. Her admirers knew precisely at what point she first appeared, and would follow her from there, while the less devoted watched her only after she came close, when nobody could resist her appeal. The boldest shouted after her, and others exchanged remarks or followed her with their eyes, lost for words. In the imagination of those shorn heads watching from behind the barbed wire, it was as if a vast nude figure of the Doe had spread over the entire hillside, flying rather than walking.

* * *

I noticed Eqerem a few days after I arrived at the camp, just after I had watched the Doe's descent for the first time. She had crossed the bridge and disappeared from view, when a tall, slender prisoner whom some called Pandi and some

'Pignose' joined his two thumbs above and his two index fingers below to form the symbol of a vagina, and shouted, 'Suzi, come on Suzi!' The prisoners who were familiar with this game made a space, and a strange creature, different from the other prisoners, came out from the crowd. As soon as he saw this vagina in the air, he removed his cap and charged towards it with head forward, as if he were going to butt his way inside. Pandi backed off a little, not allowing him to touch it, and so began Eqerem's dance. His feet and hands moved in a regular rhythm, but the main movement was of his extraordinary head, and became more aggressive and more ecstatic as it approached the 'vagina'. Pandi fell back and twirled round. Eqerem followed him with a leap, and the circle of prisoners grew wider and wider, all laughing and enjoying themselves. This scene seemed to release the tension caused by the alluring appearance of the Doe.

Eqerem's extraordinary head made his dance all the more grotesque. It led me to a discovery of a kind you can only make in prison, where heads were shorn to the scalp once a month. There are some scalps that wrap round the skull, covering it in irregular folds with deep wrinkles and furrows that a barber's razor cannot penetrate. This means that the scalp, when shorn to zero, appears mottled with pale and black patches. Spaç had about five hundred prisoners at this time, and Eqerem's was the only head of this kind. These furrows crossed the whole of his shaved head. They were shallower on his pate, and deeper at the back. Eqerem was short, with a crooked body. His face was pale and bloodless – only this kind of face, you could imagine, would fit that skull.

The prisoners said that those wrinkles were also connected to some inner disturbance, because Eqerem occasionally suffered from epileptic fits, even sometimes in the middle of his dance on the rooftop. At these times, he would start delivering a wild speech with a jumble of words that sounded like German, though only the word '*Scheisse, Scheisse*' could be distinguished. This would last about ten minutes. He would shake and snort, his eyes bulging alarmingly, and then he would suddenly collapse on the ground, trembling, shuddering, and drooling at the mouth. He would faint, and the prisoners would carry him indoors, still unconscious.

The amateur quacks in the camp claimed that this was not epilepsy, but hysteria, and happened because Eqerem had never in his life had sex. He had been sentenced to fifteen years, having attempted to flee the country by swimming out to a foreign ship that lay at the harbour entrance. He was then about twenty-five. They said he had tried to escape because his obsession was to visit a brothel in the West.

* * *

In the daily life of the camp, Eqerem was very reserved by nature, and apart from his epileptic fits and his rooftop dance, his presence disturbed nobody. None of his family came to see him, and he was therefore 'without support'. He kept a large bowl that he filled with a mush of bread and soup from the cauldron. He ate everything and never scrounged off anybody. He never argued with the guards, and they generally left him in peace.

Pandi was the only person to call to him in the name of Suzi. Everyone was astonished how he had managed to induce Eqerem to take part in such a game. If anybody else tried to call 'Suzi' to him or make the vagina sign, he would give them a furious look and make threatening gestures.

Eqerem had worked with Pandi for a long time in the same work gang, as a mallet-man. Tall 'Pignose' and another waggoner had the task of cleaning the mine-face from the debris thrown up by a blast, while Eqerem fixed the props and drilled holes in the rock. The work of the mallet-man was the hardest of all. The prisoners were scared of it, as if of a punishment, and many had refused it and even gone to the punishment cells instead. This was not because the mallet and auger together were very heavy, but because there was no wet-drilling in the mine of Spaç, and the making of the hole raised a terrible fog of dust, in which the mallet-man had to breathe for more than one hour, sometimes two, depending on the hardness of the rock. So it was usually tall and strong men who were chosen for the job of mallet-man. Eqerem was the only one, who, although short and feeble, took pleasure in this work. He insisted that if they did not give him a hammer, he would refuse even to lift a spade. When he set the mallet against his shoulder, he looked different. His entire body filled out and swelled with pride. He would turn his head to left and right so that people would see him. His white face shone and became flushed, and he was nicer to everybody. The prisoners immediately responded to this preening by teasing him, egging him on. They knew his secret pleasure. Pandi had discovered it, when one night he forgot to bring the clay which the dynamite-men used to stop the holes before the blasting, and had to take it to the face where Eqerem had begun his drilling. Usually, the waggoners kept their distance from the mallet-men as they made the holes, to avoid eating the dust: they cleared the rubble away from the face, prepared the clay, and waited below. When Pandi arrived, he noticed a curious thing amid the fog of dust raised by the mallet blows. As Eqerem drove the auger into the rock, he moved in a peculiar way. Pandi

15

drew closer, and saw how he was swept away by the pleasure of this driving motion, almost in a state of ecstasy. Despite the dust in his mouth and the deafening noise of the mallet, Pandi waited to witness the scene until the end. As he hammered with his mallet, Eqerem shook, laughed, and exulted. When the auger was driven home, and had penetrated about ninety centimetres into the rock, which was the normal depth of the holes, Eqerem thrust the mallet into his crotch and, shuddering, achieved an orgasm accompanied by howls louder even than the deafening sound of the mallet blows.

People said that Pandi's discovery of this secret turned him into Eqerem's closest and most trusted friend.

* * *

When I arrived in Spaç in 1975, Eqerem had less than one year to go. As the day of his release approached, he began to brighten and open up. Pandi teased him more and more about the happy day that was approaching, goading him on to say what he would do once he was free. Eqerem would laugh and then take him to one side to tell him what he had in mind. His most ardent wish was to bury his head in Suzi's vagina. According to Pandi, Suzi must have been a woman from Eqerem's childhood, whom he had recalled only after finding himself in prison.

Prisoners' hair was not cropped during the month before their release, so when Eqerem's day of freedom arrived, his hair had grown almost to cover the furrows in his scalp, leaving a uniform surface. Strangely this made him no less ugly, but only different.

On the morning of his release, even Eqerem performed the usual ritual of handing round cigarettes. A wide circle of prisoners would gather round to say goodbye to the departing one. A close friend distributed cigarettes to these well-wishers, and it was Pandi who handed round the cigarettes for Eqerem who, for all his ugliness, looked positively handsome that day. His face glowed. Even the patches on his head had disappeared under the brim of the new cap he had put on.

Pandi teased him a little, advising him on the sort of behaviour to win Suzi's heart. 'And don't tell her you were in prison!' he repeated. He quickly made the vagina sign and Eqerem responded with a laugh, but a gentle one, without removing his cap or starting the dance. He seemed fully aware that after that day he would have to behave in a different way, and games of that sort would not be allowed.

Before morning roll-call, they called for him to be escorted through the gate, and he left, waving farewell to everyone.

II

Three or four years had passed after Eqerem's release when news reached the camp that he'd been arrested for the second time. They said he had swum out to sea again, trying to reach a ship lying just out of the harbour. But he'd been caught halfway by the motorboats on patrol. Reportedly, he had been sentenced to another twenty years. Finally, the prison van brought him back to Spaç. On the day when we had seen him off, not many people imagined that he would find a woman and build a normal life, but nobody thought he would try to escape again.

His face was even paler. The wrinkles in his scalp were wizened, and his head was smaller, because he was thinner.

He gave no explanation of his arrest. He was now even more taciturn. In the meantime, Pandi had been released, and the Doe must have married, because we hadn't seen her for about two years.

Eqerem didn't ask to go to work, and they left him 'with 600 grams', the bread ration of the brigade without employment. He filled his big bowl less often, and his appetite wasn't what it had been. To buy odds and ends, he started sewing caps, a skill he had practised occasionally during his first sentence. He generally made white caps out of the linen foot-cloths that the camp issued to working prisoners. For these, he would ask for two or three packets of *Partizan* cigarettes. He began changing his own caps frequently, much more often than before, and he made them in a shape that hid as far as possible the back of his head where the furrows ran deepest. Some said that this frequent change of caps showed that Eqerem must have fallen in love with some young boy in the camp, but nobody could discover who it was.

Nor did he seem to suffer any longer from epileptic seizures. About a year passed, while he sewed caps and went unnoticed. But when spring came, his epileptic fits returned, reminding us of the old days. He would jump onto the third storey of bunks in the hut, and begin to rave, his eyes bulging. He would start his famous rant in German. Nobody knew why he used German for these speeches. Clearly, he wanted to assume a savage appearance, and perhaps it had something to do with the war films of his childhood, with their menacing SS men. There was always something tragic about these outbursts, and this stopped the prisoners from laughing at his meaningless jumble of German words. His fits always ended with the terrifying wail, '*Scheisse, Scheisse, Scheisse.*' Then he would fall unconscious and foam at the mouth. Now that he had come to serve his second sentence, he shrieked his gibberish in an even more tragic tone. Prisoners who had recently arrived now heard the story about the Doe and the mallet and the fact that Eqerem had never slept with a woman.

* * *

In the year when Eqerem arrived, tension was building up in the camp, as happened when times got bad. People said that this was because the dictator was very ill, and close to death. Some of the guards enforced the regulations more strictly and seemed thrilled at this opportunity to show their sadism. These were guards who provoked and tormented prisoners most. They had all worked out ways of satisfying and entertaining themselves. The officers were more subtle. Two of them in particular, the timekeeper and the pay officer, liked to 'have fun' with roll-calls.

The first would leave the prisoners standing in lines for an hour on the rooftop in the sun or rain. It was the pointlessness of this that was intolerable. The second took pleasure in issuing orders for us to parade in front of him 'at the double!' making us perform about-turns at his whim, especially when he thought we were not quick enough. But tall Nue, a sergeant who accompanied the duty officers, had a different habit. As soon as he entered with the duty officer, before the counting started, he would give the order, 'Caps off!' These continual humiliations had to be endured, because any resistance would only become cause for regret.

But this bottled-up hatred ate into the soul. One day, Fetah did not remove his cap, and after roll-call was over, they slammed him into a punishment cell for a month and gave him a thorough beating.

At no time during the whole of his first sentence had Eqerem shown any spirit of rebellion towards the guards. But then one day the unit commander, as officer on duty, came to take the roll-call. He was a serious-minded officer, who never played sadistic tricks, but also never ordered them to be stopped. Alongside him there also came tall Nue, who at once gave the order, 'Caps off!'

We could not tell how Eqerem detached himself at that moment from the assembled crowd of prisoners on the rooftop and stepped out in front of the commander. We supposed he was going to ask for something, when he began to wail in that terrifying voice we had only heard when he spoke German during his fits:

'I am a ma-a-a-a-n! I am a ma-a-a-a-n! I am a ma-a-a-a-n!'

His piercing voice, his bulging eyes, and his appeal to the commander astounded us all. The commander paled a little and took a step backwards, but stood his ground. Two guards came forward, and shoved Eqerem back in line. We imagined that he would collapse and start foaming, but he did not. The roll-call began and was completed in due order. The commander hurried to leave. The squad accompanying him, led by Nue, did not forget to take Eqerem with them, and he followed them without a word.

Clearly, he would get a month in the punishment cell, but what sort of bashing he would get, nobody knew.

* * *

They brought Eqerem out of the cell before the month was up. He came out without a cap, but with several blue stripes running across the folds on his scalp, the marks of truncheons. He didn't speak to anybody or complain. He stared without giving any reply to those who came up to him with questions. He didn't line up even for bread, and, as soon as roll-call was over, would sit in a corner of the hut, totally withdrawn into himself. He even gave up wearing a cap.

This did not last more than a few days. One morning, as we assembled on the rooftop for roll-call, we learned that Eqerem had died during the night and they had taken him away for burial early in the morning.

Tall Nue did not come out to escort the duty officer that day, and nobody gave the order to remove caps.

Ferit the Cow,
Our Partner

Not many in the camp knew Ferit's real surname. We called him 'the Cow'. To hear his real name used by one of the guards was always a surprise, as this Ferit Avdullai seemed a different person from Ferit the Cow.

* * *

Ferit was big-boned and fat, with a strange long-headed skull, protruding eyes and a broad jawbone. He even ate like a cow. At first sight, you would think this was the reason for his nickname, but in fact he was called 'the Cow' because of one of the stories, half-dream and half-reality, that Ferit kept inventing, and which passed through the camp by word of mouth.

Ferit was from the picturesque village of Lin near Pogradec on Lake Ohrid. In this sort of place, you might imagine people fishing, tending vineyards, or rowing boats, but not thieving. However, there was an agricultural cooperative, so there were cooperative thieves, and Ferit's choice in life was to be one of them. His nickname dated back to the theft of a cow from the cooperative.

Ferit told how the stolen cow had to walk through some mud, and they stuffed its hooves in two pairs of boots pointing backwards, to make false tracks. The next day, the whole village was disgusted to find the cow gone. That was Ferit's story. Later, he added a detail: the cow had refused to move, and they had put green spectacles on her nose to make the mud in front of her look like grass. That's why we called him 'the Cow', but this nickname would never have stuck, were it not for the shape of his head, his appetite, and the great pendant paunch that gave his belly such a bovine appearance.

The expression 'our partner', in the sense of belonging to the same gang, had its origin among the gypsies who used it to identify each other. It became associated with Ferit because, as the years passed, he used it to speak to almost every other prisoner. They too used it to start conversations with Ferit. 'How are you getting on, partner?' 'Fine, partner.'

Nobody had ever heard Ferit talk about a wife or children, his mother or father, or brothers and sisters. This made him the kind of prisoner whom you could not imagine with any kind of life outside prison.

Yet there were also two women whom he regularly mentioned as the loves of his life, Sanije and Xhevrije. 'Our partner Sanije' and 'Our partner Xhevrije' were phrases that Ferit used to start his stories of them. He never went into feelings of love or descriptions of sex, and seemed never to have experienced such emotions. He would instead boast of how Sanije and Xhevrije were so shrewd and canny in everyday life.

In fact, they were two well-known whores among the camps for ordinary criminals where Ferit had begun his prison life, at a very young age. He'd probably merely heard the ordinary criminals talking about them, and they had become part of his life and his fantasies.

Ferit had come to Spaç after serving several sentences for theft. Then he had been charged with agitation and propaganda against the regime. He was now over fifty, and still had about twenty years left to serve. This was because, after he came to Spaç, he was sentenced to a second term for taking part in the revolt of 1973.

Witnesses to the rebellion said that Ferit's only part in it was to attempt to loot the food store after the occupation of the camp. He didn't abandon his old trade even as a political prisoner.

The expression 'our partner' which the political prisoners used ironically, implying membership together with Ferit of the same pack of whores or thieves, seemed to aid communication on both sides. But there was in fact a great gulf between Ferit and his fellow-prisoners. 'Our partner' was a rare beast, who lived in the camp entirely according to his own laws; he used this expression more as a mask for his activities, because he knew that nobody considered him their friend. Nobody was ever seen to share a bit of bread at the same table with him. Most prisoners spoke to him only either to prompt a joke, or out of fear that he would steal from them. But nobody was safe from his pilfering; Ferit was totally unable to resist the temptation to pinch anything that caught his eye.

* * *

Ferit most often plied his trade in the washroom. It had three sections: dishes and clothes were washed in the middle, and the lavatory cubicles and showers were on either side. The washroom was one of the busiest places in the camp, because all three shifts came here at different times to wash their dishes. There was an incessant coming and going to the latrine or to wash clothes, with people also waiting in line for showers. The water fell in trickles through holes drilled in pipes, which were positioned above a sort of broad gutter raised on bricks and cement.

Above the pipes was a set of metal shelves, on which the prisoners placed their dishes or clothes while waiting their turn to wash them in the wooden tubs. It was the shelves that attracted Ferit to this place. He looked out for the flasks or plastic mugs the prisoners left there. These flasks and mugs were very valuable camp items because they were not provided by the authorities, who issued only one aluminium bowl and a spoon. Families had to bring them. They were extremely handy: the flask held drinking water or oil, and all sorts of things went into the plastic mugs. Ferit would hover about the washroom for hours on the lookout for somebody who might forget his things while absorbed in conversation, or in the lavatory. Then he would snatch his loot, stuff it in his bag, and vanish. The prisoner might notice immediately, or only the next day when he needed his flask or mug again. Then he would remember leaving it on the iron shelf. If he didn't find it there, his first thought would be to ask Ferit.

'Ever seen a flask round here, our partner?'

'No, partner.'

'There's a mugful of sugar for you if you find it, partner.'

'Let's have a look, partner. I saw a flask, but I don't know if it's yours.'

Of course, you had to hand over a portion of sugar or oil for Ferit to produce the utensil.

The washroom was also the place where Ferit was caught and ended up in solitary. This was mostly on account of Pjetër Koka, the most cunning of all the guards in tracking down prisoners' breaches of the regulations. Ferit was one of his favourite quarries. Pjetër would play cat and mouse with him, stopping him regularly and taking him to one side for a close body search. Ferit wore a camp-issue jacket with layers of patches stitched one over another. These patches also served as pockets, so he had two or three times as many pockets as on the usual camp jacket. He would hide stolen oddments in these patched pockets, which were always filthy, and secrete larger items in a bag made from the same duck cloth, also dirty and patched. In spite of the disgusting grime, Pjetër Koka thought nothing of stopping Ferit and searching him. First, he would thrust his hands into the countless pockets, and then order him to open his bag.

It was unusual for Ferit to get away without some contraband being found on him. What didn't he hide in his patches and pockets! Besides cigarette papers, which he traded freely, you might find razor blades, little pieces of mirror, nails, and stones. A sliver of razor blade or a fragment of mirror was enough to send you to a punishment cell for a month.

Pjetër Koka might let him off for a nail in his bag or pocket, but whenever he found him with a tiny mirror, he sent him straight to solitary.

Ferit's trade in mirrors was one of his most successful enterprises. Nobody knew where he found them, but he always had a few in his bag. The ban on mirrors in the camp was inexplicable, because there was no shortage of ordinary window glass that could be used to cut things. Some said it was to prevent signals being flashed outside the camp, and others that they could be used to blind the soldier in the watchtower in the course of an escape attempt, but the most likely reason was that it was one of the authorities' attempts to reduce all forms of pleasure to a minimum, like the ban on wearing civilian clothes.

The prisoners could not resist the desire to see them-selves, even in a tiny fragment of glass that showed only a part of your face. This made the trade in mirrors one of Ferit's most lucrative enterprises. Nobody knew where he found them, but if you asked him Ferit would certainly bring you one. Some prisoners said he stole them from the guards' pockets, broke them, and sold each fragment for several packets of tobacco. Ferit had his own mirror too, a little larger than the ones he sold, and you could often find him studying the deep furrows in his brow and the fatty bags under his eyes.

Ferit always submitted abjectly to Pjetër's hunting zeal. It was perhaps this very subservience that excited Pjetër's sadism as he searched him with a sour smile, certain of finding some illegal trophy. Pjetër never imagined that Ferit might resist him, and still less that this ragged figure might take his revenge one day through a fantastical story, which would turn his sadistic gratification to fury.

* * *

The camp of Spaç had four punishment cells, each about two metres long and one and a half metres wide. The inmate had to sit there the whole day, without any respite apart from the three meals, each followed by a trip to the lavatory and the issue of a cigarette. He was deprived of newspapers, books, the radio, electric light, and all food that came from his family. He was given only one ladle of broth in the morning and at midday, and one ladle of sugarless tea in the evening, with a chunk of bread. The only light in that concrete box came from the small spyhole in the door, and after dusk this was not enough to distinguish the face of a person opposite you.

Pjetër Koka called the cells 'nests'. He would threaten prisoners by saying, 'Do you miss the nest?' In summer, he would shove four or five men into each of these nests, where they sweltered in the stifling heat. In winter, he would put in one or at the most two, to prevent them warming each other with their breath and body heat. Many prisoners preferred a humiliating beating, or several hours in handcuffs screwed tight to the bone, to time in the cells. After one month in the cell, you needed two months to recover your strength.

These nests probably encouraged Ferit's rampant imagination, not only because of the extreme privations of the tiny cell, but because he had so much less chance to steal or eat. Once he came out of the cell with a dream that prisoners told to each other for a long time afterward. In his dream, Ferit had seen the craggy hills of the mine turned into mountains of pilaff. In the middle, there was a lake of yoghurt, and Ferit had eaten and drunk from these hills with a spoon made of a mine wagon. It was not clear whether this was a dream, or something that Ferit had made up, but for a long time it transformed the landscape of Spaç in the prisoners' eyes.

Ferit devised a lot of these fantasies, but didn't circulate them himself. He merely announced them when they came to him, and then somebody would pick them up and spread them round the camp. He would never retell them unless asked, and then only after persistent encouragement. However, just like his expression 'our partner', these dreams too were a mask. Nobody could discover what really went on in this man's mind. Most of Ferit's fellow-prisoners found entertainment in his stories, but our partner remained an outsider, entirely isolated. He never talked to anybody for more than a few moments at a time, and then mostly to prisoners wanting to hear his fantasies yet again, or to trade a mirror, cigarette papers, or a stolen plastic mug.

Nor did our partner show any desire to spend more time with anybody. When he started his stories, he would brighten a little, but he knew his place, and would often slope off once he had mentioned Sanije or Xhevrije, who had once made him the apple of their eye. His only significant contact with other people was through his fantasies, and it was these that determined his fate, for good or ill.

* * *

The story of the chess pieces, Ferit's most famous but also his most unfortunate tale because it sent him down to the deepest circle of hell, was in fact not a fantasy like the theft of the cow or the mountain of pilaff. It derived from an incident in a cell, which Ferit embroidered in a way that showed that this man's brain was not entirely motivated by hunger.

During one of his frequent punishments, as always after being searched by Pjetër, Ferit was put in a cell with two other prisoners, who played chess all day. The need to pass the time, which weighed upon prisoners like an invisible mountain of nothingness, led them to scratch a few lines in the planks of the floor with a sharpened spoon handle or a smuggled nail. The black squares were distinguished from the white by a few oblique lines scratched inside them. The home-made chessboards were permanent, while all the new inmates made their own pieces squeezed from breadcrumbs, with one player mixing his with cigarette ash.

Ferit was bored with these two chess players, who paid no attention to him. There was nothing there to steal or to eat, so he gobbled up the dry chess pieces while the players were dozing. They woke up and hunted for their pieces. Failing to find them, they looked at Ferit, who frankly admitted he had eaten them.

'Why did you eat them, partner?'

'I was hungry, partner. When the ration comes, I'll give you some of my bread so you can make new ones.'

They knew that when Ferit's crust came, he would devour it in an instant.

A moment later, one of the chess players noticed that there were two uneaten pieces still left on the floor.

'But why didn't you eat these two, partner?'

Ferit opened his eyes wide. Of course, he had missed them. He picked them up. One was a pawn and the other a bishop.

I didn't eat these,' he said, 'because this little one looked like that nice Lazër, and this bishop looked like Ali.'

Lazër was the most decent of the camp guards, while Ali was the camp bookkeeper, who was always very courteous and spoke little to the prisoners.

The incident became famous in the camp. 'But which one did you eat first?' the prisoners asked when Ferit came out. 'Pjetër Koka,' Ferit replied.

After this story, Ferit was forgiven all the harm he'd done, pinching rubber mugs, flasks, and other odd and ends. This joke brought Ferit closer to his fellow-prisoners than at any time before, but he paid a heavy price for it. The rumour that Ferit had eaten all the officers and guards, except for Ali and little Lazër, reached the ears of the authorities. One of Pjetër Koka's many spies passed it on to him, and the latter reacted with his nasty smile, 'I will send Ferit Avdullai down to a place where he won't have a chance to eat or steal or make jokes like that.'

He meant Burrel Prison, which was sheer hell for prisoners like Ferit without help from their families. In the camp they at least breathed fresh air, were tanned by the sun, and could cook up something to eat. They could obtain cigarettes because there were hundreds of prisoners and a huge kitchen which also cooked for the mineworkers. But in Burrel prison the regime was entirely different. There were only two hours of exercise, and you spent the remaining twenty-two cooped inside your cell with a bunch of other prisoners. The food was the minimal ration allotted to non-working prisoners, and anyone who couldn't lose himself in a book perished from boredom.

They soon found the opportunity to send him to Burrel.

'Our partner' was not aggressive or violent. When you caught him with your mug, he would say at once that he hadn't known it belonged to 'our partner' and give it to you without a murmur. So the whole camp was surprised one day when he pulled a stone out of his bag and hit Fetah on the head. It was a few days before Fetah was due to be released. He ended up in the sick bay, and soon left, and so nobody heard the reason why Ferit had hit him. The story went that Fetah had beaten him up many years previously and Ferit had waited to take revenge until just before his release, so that Fetah would have no time to pay him back. We all knew that our mate had the courage of a chicken, but nobody believed that he could harbour a grudge for so long. In fact, nobody knew what was on Ferit's mind that day.

Some said that Fetah, with a raging thirst, had hogged the tap for half an hour, and left Ferit to wait so long that he lost his temper. But we could not believe this either. The secret behind this blow lay hidden in Ferit's impenetrable depths. He spent another month in solitary and they sent him to Burrel as soon as he came out.

Everybody was surprised, but then remembered Pjetër Koka's vow. The blow to Fetah's head became Pjetër's pretext to strike in revenge for the story of the chess pieces. This tale successfully went the rounds not only in Spaç but beyond, as transferred prisoners carried it to other camps and prisons.

* * *

Ferit received a warm welcome from the prisoners of Burrel, because his fantastical stories had gone before him from Spaç. The prisoners immediately began to call him 'our partner' and he would tell them about the many skills of Sanije and Xhevrije. He was even able to get his teeth into some food from family parcels, because the custom in Burrel was that anybody who had a visit would treat each of his roommates. But there were not many visitors to Burrel and there were no more than ten prisoners to a room, most of them bored and hungry.

Ferit very soon understood what he had brought on himself by eating the entire guard detachment of Spaç and especially Pjetër Koka. His main desire now was to find tobacco: in the camp his trade in mirrors and odds and ends had kept him supplied. Now he began selling his bread ration to buy handfuls of tobacco, and for food he relied on leftovers given to him by prisoners who received visits or large parcels. When he was short, he would collect the dog-ends of cigarettes. He would cut them open, dry the contents, and smoke them rolled in newspaper.

As time passed, his hunger became more ravenous, but he couldn't easily steal. He was under his fellow-prisoners' gaze all day. He began to waste away; his ribs showed, and his nickname 'the Cow' fitted him better than ever. One of his ribs was indeed as thick as a cow's. Yet strangest of all was his physical immunity. When any of the food brought by their families spoiled, his roommates would testily throw it into the garbage pail in the corner. They wouldn't dare give it to Ferit for fear of poisoning him, even though he begged for it so persistently. Ferit himself would retrieve it from the pail, and eat it. Amazingly, nothing ever happened to him.

But this man was insatiable. His mind got to work on schemes to obtain food through his original trade of theft. But how to steal in a room where you were always in the company of your fellow-prisoners?

So Ferit began to suffer a calvary of beatings at the hands of the other prisoners. The first to beat him up was a prisoner with no parcels. While waiting to fetch his soup from the canteen, he had left his bowl near the door, and was finishing a game of chess. There were two spoonfuls of oil in the bowl which another prisoner had given to him to thicken the prison broth. Meanwhile, Ferit paced back and forth from the wall to the door with his bread ration in his hand, and whenever he passed the bowl, he would dip his bread in the oil and continue his pacing, munching the oil-smeared crust. After he had passed several times, somebody noticed this and shouted at him. The other prisoner found that the oil had gone from his bowl. In the camp, this might be taken as a joke, but not in Burrel. The victim seized his bowl and struck Ferit on the head with it several times. Our partner did not react.

The beatings became more frequent. Prisoners with family visits, who had been generous to him in the past, were the angriest of all; Ferit would promise not to touch their food, and still they found themselves robbed. Ferit never struck back, but only protected himself, covering his head with his hands. Normally he came off lightly because the beatings were perfunctory. There was no time for the guard to come, open the spyhole, and catch the assailants in the act.

When he found he could not hide any of his thefts, Ferit chose another method. He stayed awake at night and after everyone had fallen asleep, he would get up and rummage among the bags of food that the prisoners kept under the bed-boards. The prisoners would discover their food was gone after they had used the bathroom and were waiting for the door to open for breakfast. Some prisoners would shout at him, but they couldn't beat him, for the guard would come at any moment and they would land in a punishment cell immediately. Yet they knew that 'our partner' had stolen from them. This was more a form of plunder than theft, and Ferit admitted that it was hunger that drove him to it.

One day when they returned from one hour in the exercise yard, his cell-mates discovered that all their bags were gone. Nobody had noticed that Ferit had come out for exercise a little late. During those few moments, he had gobbled everything inside them, and taken the bags and stuck them under the steps that went down to the exercise yard, where they were later found by the cleaner.

This time, several people jumped on him. Ferit bent his back, hid his head under his arms, and endured it all without making a sound. The prisoners vented all their fury. The guard did not interrupt, though he must have been in the exercise yard. Then they hung back. They thought they had beaten him black and blue, but amazingly Ferit stood up and straightened his back. He started hunting all over the place, bending his head to the floor and muttering, 'Where did I drop that cigarette? Where did I drop that cigarette?' – It was the cigarette he had lit before they jumped upon him.

Because he provoked fights of this kind the authorities started moving Ferit from one room in the prison to another. His presence in any room made life a nightmare. In Spaç, the prisoners had been able to keep their distance from him, but here the presence of this man with a ravenous beast inside him was just too exhausting. Anyone in the same room as Ferit simply had to leave his food in the storehouse outside. There was no way of breaking the monotony of the day by eating something in your room. Or you had to be on permanent watch. Worse, in each of the rooms where Ferit went, a prisoner would end up in a punishment cell on his account, because sooner or later someone would beat him up and be caught by the guard. Prisoners became convinced that the governor was using Ferit to punish the inmates he disliked.

Yet Ferit himself often ended up in the cells too. It was when he came out of one of the cells in winter that he told his most famous fantasy during his time in Burrel. It was freezing cold in the cell. The icicles hanging from the prison roof penetrated the grille, and hung down close to his head. His belly was racked by hunger. One night he saw himself in a dream, covered by a great quilt made of pastry. Hungrily, he started to eat the upper edge that covered his neck. But this made the crust smaller, and his feet stuck out from the bottom and froze. All night long, he wrestled with the pastry, eating it from the top and stretching it with his feet at the bottom. He had devoured it all when dawn came and he woke up frozen to the bone.

For a time, this fantastical dream eased his relations with his fellow-prisoners. They cheerfully overlooked some of his nightly thefts.

But their earlier hostility soon returned when Ferit became the reason why not one but two prisoners were sent to the cells. One of the prisoners who had received a visit from his family gave Ferit his share of the general ration and made Ferit promise that he wouldn't touch the bag under his bed that night. But Ferit couldn't resist the piece of meat he had caught sight of. He got up in the night and ate it. Moreover, he refused to take the blame, but accused two other prisoners who slept opposite him, who then went wild with rage and threw themselves onto him, punching and kicking. The guard opened the spyhole at that very moment, caught them in the act, and one hour later took the men away and threw them in a cell.

The entire room was furious. They could stomach no more. When the guard closed the door, leading his two most recent victims away to the cells, the inmates of the room devised a plan. They would beat Ferit to the verge of death. Ferit's final victim, who had lost all the meat brought by his family, got ready for action by putting on a pair of army boots. Ferit sat on his bed, guiltily hanging his head, unaware of the beating in store, the likes of which he had never known. One prisoner threw a blanket over Ferit's head, and the others leapt on him, attacking him with boots and fists in a frenzy.

He was thrown from his bunk to the ground. The guard opened the spy-hole, but still the prisoners didn't stop. This time, they had decided they would all go to the cells. At times like this, the guards did not interfere. Ferit lay on the floor, the prisoners kicking him all over his body, and in the head. But they knew from experience that he always bounced back. The prisoner in the army boots whose food Ferit had stolen climbed onto the bunks and hurled himself with his full weight on Ferit's body, again and again, until he heard a crack. The men fell back. Ferit lay still. Not a sound came from him. He had never before failed to stand up after a beating. Now that the uproar was over, the guard opened the door and ordered the prisoners to put him outside.

The doctor diagnosed severe bruising, two broken ribs, and a serious fracture of the pelvis. Ferit was sent urgently to the prison hospital.

* * *

When Ferit came out of the hospital several months later, he was sent back not to Burrel but to the camp. Strangely, he no longer stole and had lost his insatiable appetite. He made do with the camp rations and the occasional morsel he was given. Nor did he tell any fantastical stories. He was an ordinary prisoner who had suddenly discovered that he was an old man. If one of the long-term prisoners who had known him in the past asked him to tell how he had eaten the chess pieces, or the dreams with the mountains of pilaff or the pastry quilt, he would sit and listen as if these stories had nothing to do with him.

It was only when you mentioned Sanije and Xhevrije that he would smile a little and say, yes, they knew what life was all about and how to give a man a good time.

Kujtim

'Steer clear of that character!' warned a veteran prisoner, as I parted from another inmate after walking for half an hour on the rooftop parade ground.

'Is he a spy?' I asked.

'No, he's not a spy.'

'Then what's the matter with him?'

'You'll find out later. He probably talked to you about poetry.'

'Yes. What's this all about?'

'I'll say no more. You're new to prison.'

* * *

Kujtim, the man to whom I was supposed to give a wide berth, had approached me and started a conversation as I was walking by myself on the rooftop. He was about thirty-five, bald, slightly built, and with a rather weary expression. He told me that he had spent almost twenty years in prison. He seemed quiet and relaxed in conversation. His Albanian was different to that of most prisoners, educated, with polished phrases. He was interested to know what young people were thinking in Tirana, their enthusiasms, how they spent their free time, whether they learned foreign languages, and read literature. Then he said that he himself wrote poetry and made a few remarks about some of our best-known writers, whom he despised for being in the service of the regime.

Then the conversation ended because the crier gave the shout for roll-call.

I inevitably thought that if the warning to steer clear of this man was not because he was a spy, it must be something to do with the reason why new arrivals in prison were called 'meat'. A few days in prison were enough to tell you that in this brutal all-male society, you had to keep a distance from hunters of meat, as homosexuals were called. From the very start, old lags warned you that these men were the most dangerous characters in prison, after the spies. Listening to their advice, the images instilled in childhood through stories and vulgar language, which portrayed homosexuals as disgusting and frightening, acquired the ugliest shapes in the imagination.

'No, no,' they said when you asked for more details. 'It's not like in ordinary prisons here, where they can rape you in the mine gallery. That can happen here, of course, but the worst of it is that if you keep company with them, everybody in the camp will see you as a woman, not a man, and will despise you, do you down, and laugh at you as a pervert, a bumboy, and arse-peddler. It's a mark of shame, hard to bear if you want to be treated with human dignity.'

After these warnings, any young prisoner who saw that he was being stalked by a 'pervert' who saw him as a woman and was in danger of being mocked as a queer, had to show he was nothing of the sort. Otherwise, he had to accept humiliations that were worse even than those suffered by prisoners who had agreed to become spies. Informing was at least a man's business, whereas to be fucked in the arse was only for women. For this reason, there were different attitudes to active and passive homosexuals. The active sort, mostly elderly prisoners, prompted greater disgust, mingled with fear, while the passive sort were viewed with disgust mingled with contempt.

* * *

However, when I delved more deeply into the rumours circulating round the prison, I discovered that not even the prisoners who were known to be homosexual carried the same fearful aura as Kujtim. You would see them in the company with other prisoners, and of course in the camp it was easy to find someone eager to boast of their sexual exploits. But Kujtim was surrounded by a silence that made him frightening. The prisoner who had warned me away from him did not broach the subject of Kujtim again, and for a time nobody spoke to me openly against him. People implied that I shouldn't go near him, without making clear why.

It took some time before I got to know Bajram, who was among those who didn't talk to Kujtim, and I learned the reason why this slightly built man with his cultivated speech and passion for poetry cast such a dark shadow and struck such fear into his fellow-prisoners. Kujtim had committed a murder, in the prison itself, and had killed his friend with whom he shared his bread. This had happened many years ago, soon after he'd started his sentence.

* * *

Kujtim had been born in a mountain village, of the kind where they say 'the hens eat pebbles', and apparently this poor start had set his life on a disastrous course. His efforts to escape his bad luck only led him deeper into trouble. When he finished seventh grade elementary school, he tried to escape from Albania. They caught him near the border, entirely on his own, and convicted him of treason to the homeland.

Nobody ever found out what had impelled him to run away from his family at that age. Kujtim himself said that he had done so because his family had been labelled kulaks, and for this reason he was debarred from high school and he didn't want to end his days as a farm labourer in the remote village where he was born. But others said he had run away after a brutal beating from his father, had left home without knowing where he was going, and after he was caught, because he didn't want to be returned home, had said he was trying to escape.

Taking into account his youth, they sentenced him to five years, half the minimum sentence for escape, and sent him to serve his sentence in the so-called 'vocational prison' in the capital city This prison usually held less dangerous prisoners, who had easier work than those who laboured in swamp-drainage, mining, or construction. They produced shoes and clothes for the army, the police, and all the prisons, both for political prisoners and ordinary criminals.

There, Kujtim formed a close friendship with a young lad, a few years older than himself. It was one of those close prison relationships: they started learning French from an elderly prisoner, ate their meals together, and slept in adjacent beds. Young prisoners often formed these friendships, involving very strong feelings of love, self-sacrifice, and loyalty. The rules for these friendships were the same as those for family. You had to consider the friend with whom your shared your meals to be your brother; if anybody touched or struck him, you had to defend him and take revenge as for your brother. But these relationships also encouraged rumours of homosexuality.

* * *

The fraternal relationship between Kujtim and his friend had continued until one day the prisoners were stunned by incredible news: Kujtim had killed his friend in the cruellest and most terrifyingly cold-blooded fashion: after battering him to death, he had gouged out his eyes.

Telling me the story, Bajram said that the murder took place twenty years ago, without any witness. According to the prisoners of the time, on the day of the murder Kujtim's friend left his workplace to go to the bathroom and never returned. His absence was only noticed at roll-call after the shift, when the prisoners were counted before entering the zone of the canteen and dormitories.

The prison guards launched a search, fearing he had escaped. After about an hour, they discovered his mutilated corpse among the machines of the tailoring shop, with the empty eye sockets staring at the ceiling.

There was a bloodstain under the victim's head and other wounds to his face, throat and chest. When they moved him, they found that the blood had come from a blow from a bar to the back of the head. The suspicion arose that at least two people had been involved in the killing: one person had hit the victim from behind with an iron bar, and the other had finished the job with knives. The wounds also indicated that at least two knives had been used. But no murder implements were found at the scene of the crime. There was only a tailor's thimble such as the prisoners used in that workshop.

The prisoners were locked up in the dormitories and the search for the knives and the iron bar went on all night. There were also 'informational procedures' as they called hearing reports from the authorities' spies. Six people were detained in the early hours, including Kujtim. It was said they had been noticed spending a lot of time together during the preceding few days, as if they were cooking up something. The thimble also played a role in their detention, because all six were from the tailoring shop. But a few days later five of them were released from solitary.

Only Kujtim was left in a cell, accused of murder. A few weeks later it was reported that he had admitted to the crime, explaining it because his friend had tried to rape him, threatening him with a knife.

In fact, he didn't use the word rape, but dishonour. Kujtim said that in self-defence he had taken an iron bar which was at hand and struck him with it, and then reached for a knife and killed him. But the investigators still didn't believe this version. They had no doubt the murder was premeditated. Later Kujtim admitted that the knife was his own, but he always denied that he had accomplices.

* * *

When they talked about this murder, the prisoners consistently mentioned one strange fact. According to witnesses at the time, Kujtim, immediately after the murder, had calmly eaten lunch, in a manner impossible to believe of an adolescent who had just committed such a terrible act. Indeed, according to the guards of the investigators' cells, he continued to eat with total composure. This equanimity and the gouging of the eyes, Bajram said, showed that Kujtim deserved his reputation in the prison as a born criminal.

But some said that there was another explanation for the gouged eyes and Kujtim's cool head, and that the motivation for the killing had been misunderstood for twenty years. According to this version, Kujtim wasn't the killer. His friend had been murdered by other people who had discovered he was a spy who would denounce their plan for escape. Kujtim had taken the blame on himself because he was young and couldn't be sentenced to death.

Even the gouging of the eyes wasn't an act of hatred, but an attempt by the murderers to cover their tracks. Those who had killed him believed in a tale that was circulating in prison at that time that the image of the last person a dying man sees remains imprinted on the pupil of the eye. So they had cut out his eyes to remove the image of the man the victim was talking to, while another man struck him on the back of the head with an iron bar.

But Bajram didn't believe this version. How could Kujtim, who had the shortest possible sentence, shoulder blame for a crime that would keep him in prison for the rest of his life? Also, if this were the case, the true culprits wouldn't have remained undiscovered.

No, Kujtim had killed him because of sexual advances, perhaps helped by others, but definitely for this motive.

'To understand what happened,' he said to me one day, 'imagine what it means to fall into prison at his age.'

'What do you mean by that?' I asked.

'He hadn't yet grown hair on his chin, and he had no experience with a woman.'

Bajram told me that it was a rare event for such a young boy to arrive at the prison.

'This wasn't just a delivery of meat, but of super-meat. Do you understand? Plenty of prisoners would frantically desire a boy like that. Some would approach him directly, but others would watch him from a distance and gossip about him. Predators of this kind would call him by a woman's name or the name of a flower, Mimoza or Vjollca. Fortunately, I was as ugly as a monkey and when I arrived nobody came near me,' he added with a loud laugh. But perhaps they gave even me a nickname. Monkey would have suited me.'

Then he became serious again and explained to me what he thought had happened. Most probably his friend had touched him up during the night while he slept, and Kujtim, offended, had devised a plan and killed him on his own without telling anybody. Or perhaps some jealous prisoner had spread the false rumour that his friend was claiming all over the place that he was his lover.

The prison was full of intrigues cooked up by those lusting after young boys. Sexual hunger was like the lava of a volcano, which except in a very few cases never erupted onto the surface but seethed underground, a suppressed source of energy.

The predators kept company in groups of two and three and hunted young boys from a distance. Sometimes there were conflicts in these groups over a boy. Indeed, when one of them was taken under the protective wing of a prisoner or a group, his protectors went wild with desire for this 'meat'. Most of the young boys just ignored the rumours spread about them, even when they were brought to their attention. But there were others, prouder and tougher, who would not put up with them. To show that they had no intention of being treated as women, some put up their fists, and others struck anyone who pestered them with a stick, a stone, or a brick to the head. But only Kujtim had gone as far as murder. Even the most fanatical found it hard to understand how anyone could go so far as to kill while defending male honour.

'Unless there was something deeper in that relationship,' said someone who had been in the vocational prison, without saying any more.

'But how can someone who has killed for this become a predator himself?' I asked.

'It happens, it happens! Sexual hunger sometimes drives people crazy. Particularly in cases like Kujtim and myself, who arrived in prison without ever having touched a woman.'

'But it hasn't driven you crazy.'

'It has, but differently. I've become a hermaphrodite. I put my cock between my thighs and get my rocks off that way.'

* * *

Nobody ever heard the truth from Kujtim's own lips. Nor did anyone find out what he had said in court. This slightly built lad came back to the camp, sentenced to twenty-five years and with the aura of a frightening criminal. It would now be hard for anyone to see him as a woman.

But as you learned more about his story, it became clear that it was not just this appalling murder that had isolated Kujtim from his fellow-prisoners. They said that after this first tragedy he had again formed a close friendship. It was the grim end of this second relationship that had turned him into an accursed figure who aroused irrational fear, as if even going near him could bring you to grief.

When Kujtim turned eighteen, they transferred him to the camp at Rubik, where the prisoners were constructing a copper smelting plant. There, aged twenty-three, he became friends with a young prisoner a few years older than himself. This prisoner had been brought to Rubik after attempting an escape from a camp for ordinary criminals. He had been caught and sentenced to twenty-five years for treason. Nobody knew how they formed this friendship, but soon they kept company only with each other.

One day they both decided to escape from the camp to Yugoslavia. Clearly the endless years they had still to serve led them to this decision, but there was more. They were much more likely to lose their lives than succeed in this plan, but they were courageous characters who wouldn't submit to fate. Kujtim had shown that when he was fifteen.

The second escape attempt was additional evidence for those who believed that the motive for the murder had been to cover up the escape attempt from the vocational prison. Some had said that Kujtim had only four years left on his sentence when he committed the murder, and so had no reason to join an escape attempt, but they forgot that for a sixteen-year-old boy, four years are as long as ten for an adult, and that he had started his escape attempts aged fifteen.

* * *

Kujtim and his friend devised their plan after noticing that the perimeter guards didn't always take their automatic rifles to their watchtowers, but sometimes only ordinary rifles. Kujtim's friend, who had done military service, said that if they ran through the zone under the surveillance of the watchtower at night, they would be unlikely to be shot from a rifle, as opposed to a Kalashnikov that fired a hail of bullets. There was no way that ordinary soldiers like these guards could be snipers.

They noticed that one of the camp huts used as a storehouse greatly reduced the field of vision from the watch tower. If they walked in its shadow, they could come very close to the perimeter fence without being seen. Then they could make their dangerous dash, quickly pass through the wire and hide behind some rocks at the entrance to the forest that began a few metres beyond.

They carried out this operation one night when the duty guard had arrived with a rifle. He saw them and cried 'Halt!' three times and then fired several bullets without hitting them. They managed to reach the forest and cover their tracks. All night they wandered through the forest, and crossed a hill, descending to the shore of a lake where they found a rowing boat they used to reach a village on the opposite bank.

Towards dawn they came across a villager whom they asked for help. He seemed a poor and simple man and they trusted him. He gave them bread and they promised him they would give him money if he sheltered them until the commotion of the search party, which had no doubt spread over the whole area, had subsided.

The villager hid them in a cowshed, but the next day, under pressure from a member of his family, he denounced them to their pursuers, and so they were caught.

They sentenced Kujtim's close friend to death, because of his repeated escape attempts, and extended Kujtim's sentence by another twenty-five years. This branded him for ever as a tragic figure.

* * *

As time passed, I saw that Kujtim, just as he had approached me, would draw near to other new prisoners arriving at Spaç. It was soon clear that they too, in one way or another, received the warnings that I had been given, and kept away from him after the first conversation. Many prisoners followed from a distance, with sadistic pleasure, his failed attempts to approach newcomers. When they saw a first meeting followed by a second, they would worry, and the most likely reason was that the newcomer's acquaintances had not done their duty. Then, when they saw Kujtim walking alone on the rooftop again, they would smile with satisfaction. And so, he became increasingly closed in on himself and spent his free time reading or writing poetry.

He met very rarely those few people who spoke to him, who included myself. His passion for literature and poetry encouraged me not to break off all contact with him, although I met him less frequently after Bajram's warning. Often, we didn't walk together for weeks. But he was used to being kept at arm's length by the other prisoners. He knew well whom he could speak to, and at what times and for how long he could talk to them without making them anxious. He rarely made the mistake of imposing himself on somebody for whom he wasn't welcome. And so I kept track of him with particular curiosity, because he was one of the extraordinary people who, once you have got to know them and learned their story, capture your attention forever.

When we met, he would recite the new poems he had written. These poems had short, rhyming lines. He told me that he wrote them down on paper, but memorised them and tore up the manuscript, not only because in most of his poems he cursed the dictatorship and our own misfortunes, but because there was a close search every two weeks in the camp, and if they found written poems they would take them from you, whatever they were about, and send you to a punishment cell. One day Kujtim told me that he had two volumes in his head.

'I have them as if written in a book on separate pages that I can leaf through,' he said when I asked him how he remembered them. 'And sometimes I recite the whole book to myself.'

Very occasionally he would correct some poems, taking out a word or inserting a better rhyme. Bajram said that he also wrote love poems about boys to whom he gave girls' names. Bajram knew this because when Kujtim was younger, he would recite these poems as if they were his dreams of love, but he didn't do this any longer.

I remember one of his poems that he recited to me at this time, which was about the two passions of his life, his love of 'reckless heroes' and of knowledge and poetry. He described these two passions as fighting for dominance in his mind, without either defeating the other.

Many prisoners were surprised to see a newly-arrived, young, and good-looking prisoner gradually spending more and more time with Kujtim regardless of the advice of his elders. They stepped up their warnings, but Plato, as he was called, paid no attention, and he established a strong friendship with Kujtim. The last to take the courage to warn him came back smiling bitterly at this lad's naivety:

'Kujtim is one of the kindest people I've met in my life,' he had announced, and cut the conversation short.

At first, they considered the lad to be simple, but then started insulting him as a pervert who had already learned homosexual ways before he came to prison and was probably also a spy.

Meanwhile, Kujtim was behaving in ways that reminded old prisoners of his two earlier tragic relationships. Whenever possible, he kept company only with Plato. When the two worked on different shifts, he would wait for Plato to come out of the mine gallery, cook for him in the private kitchen, and wash his clothes. The two could not be separated, except when the camp schedule required it.

After a while, rumours spread that they had been seen kissing in the mine. Some asserted moreover that contrary to general belief, it was Kujtim who played the woman's role and Plato the man's.

What was going on? The story of the murder surfaced again, with all the old questions surrounding it. Was this a man who had murdered to defend his male honour, but now was not only mixed up in homosexuality but playing the role of a woman? Or had the story been different all along?

This third relationship prompted Bajram to tell me the comment of a prisoner who had been at the vocational prison at the time of the murder. He was a wise man, he said, one of the intellectuals that the regime had put in prison after World War Two and never let out.

'The love of one man for another can be spiritual, like the love of a man for a woman,' he had said to Bajram, who opened his eyes wide.

The prison talk about older prisoners seeing young boys as women and solely as sexual provender excluded the possibility of a spiritual tie between them. However, he had noticed strong signs of a spiritual relationship between these two. Kujtim's motive for the murder might have been the jealousy of a young man who is in love for the first time. Wildly in love, Kujtim had gone crazy when his friend had cast his eyes on someone else and had killed him.

If one believed this interpretation, his escape from prison with his second friend could also be explained differently. It wasn't a desire for freedom, but love of his friend that impelled Kujtim to escape with him, so they would be tied together forever, and save their love from that stifling environment.

'But I don't believe this version,' Bajram said.

'He committed his murder because he felt ashamed in his own eyes and those of others, because they might have seen him as weak, as a bumboy. He wanted to show the others that they couldn't make fun of him or despise him. And so now he doesn't talk to anybody about this. Maybe he experienced love for men later and he may have repented, but he doesn't say.'

Meanwhile the whole camp was waiting for the incident that would put an end to his relationship with Plato. It was not long in coming.

* * *

Among the most famous of the old prisoners were two brothers, who were mostly called by the nicknames 'the Limper' and 'Deaf-Boy'. When in their twenties, they had both tried to escape together, but they were caught at the border and each sentenced to twenty-five years for treason. Apparently, they had been caught because a border guard had fired and hit the Limper, and Deaf-Boy had stopped to help his brother.

When Plato arrived, they had about fifteen years of prison behind them. They had acquired their nicknames because of their two disabilities. Deaf-Boy, who was the elder, always put his hand to his ear as if to catch the sound-waves of what people were saying. The Limper walked unsteadily because the bullet had damaged his left leg.

Deaf-Boy was reticent and hardworking, but the Limper was the opposite. He was a great joker and talked to everybody. He had a reputation as a hunter after 'meat' and his greatest jokes were about this. But it was never clear whether these were mere humour or expressions of his ravenous sexual hunger. His most frequent joke was turning the young boys who arrived in the camp into women. His description recalled the scene in Charlie Chaplin's *Gold Rush* in which two characters snowbound in a hut have nothing to eat. The fat character pretends that his comrade is a chicken and makes as if to kill and eat him.

'Pretty boys turn into women when I see them,' said the excited Limper as he told his jokes. Then I blink and they're boys again, and then I blink again and they're women.'

* * *

The Limper, when he saw that Plato was not going to turn his back on Kujtim despite all his warnings, started praising his lovely backside and legs, and how, if he laid his hands on him, he would eat him alive, flesh and bone. Some listeners found his fantasy to be too vivid to be a joke, but others said that this was his way of expressing something he felt, but could never act on. Seeing Plato's friendship with Kujtim, the Limper became convinced he was a likely candidate and started to tease him. Then he went further, and when he came across Plato, he would make innuendos, winking and saying that Kujtim was not the right man for him, then brushing against him with his body and putting his hands and mouth close.

The Limper's game caused the third fatal incident in Kujtim's life in prison.

Even though the Limper was physically very strong and frightening when provoked, Plato decided to do something to get rid of this annoying man. One day, when the Limper was making his usual advances, Plato went up to him, as if to respond, and suddenly punched him on the chin. They were on the edge of a drop that fell away several metres from the canteen square to the foundations of the dormitory. The Limper fell, but pulled down Plato with him. The two rolled downhill together. When they reached the bottom, Plato was on top, and he reached for a sharp stone and struck the Limper several times on the head with all his strength. He left the Limper lying there stunned and went to give himself up to the guards.

The Limper recovered quickly, and rushed after Plato in fury, his head soaked in blood. He looked for him everywhere, but couldn't find him. Deaf-Boy, seeing his brother in this state, joined him in search of Plato. They entered the washroom and found Kujtim there washing clothes, unaware of anything that had happened. Without any explanation, they brutally attacked him with their fists. The more blood poured from the Limper's own head, the more he struck the head of the finely built Kujtim until he fell unconscious to the ground. They kicked him in the head with their full strength. Nobody dared intervene until Deaf-Boy pulled away his brother, seeing that Kujtim was not moving. Two other men picked him up from the concrete floor of the washroom and carried him up to the sick bay.

It was a different Kujtim that the prisoners now saw in front of them, his head horribly swollen, double its size from the punches and kicks.

* * *

They put the Limper and Plato in separate punishment cells and gave them the maximum of one month solitary. They excluded Deaf-Boy, because he claimed he had intervened merely to separate the other two. Kujtim was sent to the clinic and kept under observation for a week. When he was released, there were still black cuts on his head.

After a month each in solitary, the Limper and Plato were brought face to face with one another in front of the commander. They were told either to take a punishment for assault and be sent to Burrel prison, or to return to the camp and promise not to continue their quarrel. They chose the latter.

The prisoners were waiting to see how Kujtim would respond. In this story, Kujtim the untouchable criminal had been purely a victim. A month or two passed and the incident seemed forgotten. People thought that Kujtim was so close to Plato that he would not risk an act of revenge that might lead to being deprived of his intimacy with him, especially considering how physically weak he was compared to the Limper. But one day he provided another piece of evidence to those who argued that he had killed in defence of his male honour and not for love.

At roll-call, when all the prisoners were hurrying into line to be counted, he came up to the Limper from behind and struck him with full force on the back of the head with a big stone he took out of a bag, aiming to kill. The Limper crumpled to the ground, and lay unconscious. After a while he came round.

The guards seized Kujtim at once and threw him in a punishment cell. When he finished his one-month sentence, the prison commander brought him out of the cell and put him in front of all the assembled prisoners, asking him to show remorse for what he had done. Kujtim had been sentenced first for attempted escape, then murder, then escape again and now attempted murder, but he didn't accept that he had done anything wrong.

A few days later they took him away to the punitive regime of Burrel. As he left, I remembered his poem about his two passions and thought that his love for reckless heroes had defeated his love for knowledge and poetry. But I was mistaken.

* * *

Prisoners transferred from Burrel to the camp said that Kujtim cut a very lonely figure. He spent all day reading and translating whatever books came to hand. He rarely joined his cellmates' conversation but never bothered anybody.

Perhaps for this reason they took him out of Burrel after a few years and brought him back to Spaç.

By now he had spent almost thirty years in prison. Plato had been released, and the Limper had been transferred to the camp at Ballsh. To those of us who had known him, Kujtim's physical decline was striking. Although he was not yet fifty, he looked seventy. On the journey to Spaç in the prison van he had thrown up several times and fainted. He complained of a host of ailments, and his high blood pressure could kill him at any moment. His body was racked with all kinds of pains. An imprisoned doctor said that the blows to his head from the Limper and Deaf-Boy had led to brain damage.

The old prisoners welcomed him with more kindness than before. Some of his personal enemies had now been released. Bajram too had been freed, and indeed news had come that he had married a prisoner's daughter. Prisoners who arrived after Kujtim's transfer to Burrel were amazed to learn he had served thirty years in prison, and their eyes widened in respect. He carried an aura of mystery. Not many people recalled his crime of murder. Some prisoners still watched him to see if he would approach the boys, but after a while it appeared he was not interested in making new acquaintances. He kept company only with older prisoners whom he had known before his transfer to Burrel.

* * *

As soon as I got the chance to sit down with him and have a long conversation, Kujtim told me that Burrel prison was the darkest pit he had known in all his years in the camps and prisons, because of his extreme loneliness there. Yet this very solitude had illuminated his mind. He had found some old books passed down by generations of prisoners. The two books he continually mentioned were one with seven tragedies of Sophocles in French and a book on the history of classical philosophy that prisoners had translated into Albanian, who knows when. Kujtim had translated the seven tragedies of Sophocles and reread the book of philosophy several times.

'But above all,' he said to me, 'I've thought about my own life while reading these books.'

Nor had he given up his passion for poetry in Burrel. He had written more than in the camp and stored all the poems in his memory. He recited some to me, and I was struck by the difference compared to the poems that I remembered from the time before Burrel. In the earlier ones too, he was burdened by the thought of the misfortunes he had suffered and the relationship between these misfortunes and the choices he had made in trying to escape them. But if in the earlier poems he strongly resisted fate, and was at war against it in a struggle he believed he could win, in the Burrel poems he saw his adversities as a destiny dictated by the gods. Instead of a struggle, there was a sense of surrender, reconciliation, and a search for spiritual peace. He evidently saw himself as similar to Sophocles' heroes, who after rebelling and striving to oppose the will of the gods, surrender to it.

In the period before Burrel, two forces had pulled his life in opposite directions: love of knowledge and poetry, and love for 'reckless heroes'. He described these two ideals as if they coexisted in a battle against each other, as if the strand of his life was held in tension between them. Now it was as if the cord was broken and the two passions, weary of their struggle, had made peace. He didn't hope for any wisdom beyond what he learned in prison and he couldn't escape the misfortunes that his passion for 'reckless heroes' had caused him.

Before Burrel, he compared his poems to a balm that relieved at least to some extent the wounds caused by his suffering. He believed that these wounds would heal and he would write about other things. But in the Burrel poems the wounds and the balm had become one and the same thing, because without the wounds he wouldn't be writing the poems. If earlier he had dreamed of living in other countries where he would write different poems, he now thought that it no longer made sense to imagine a different life: he loved the poems that he had written about these wounds and seemed almost to love the wounds because of these poems.

'The greatest wisdom lies in loving only those things that happen to us, that are woven into the fabric of our lives,' he said, quoting the Stoics whom he had read in Burrel.

He wasn't always so stoical. One day he recited to me several poems in which he compared spiritual peace to a frozen tear which sometimes melted and coursed down his face, prompting a flood of feelings of anxiety and bitter memories. He would curse a life lived for nothing, without love. As he recited these poems to me, I remembered his love poems to the men he had given women's names. I thought of these poems as imprisoned in his mind without hope of ever being released, because they were watched by a very strict guard who held in his hand, like a key, the murder that Kujtim had committed.

* * *

Kujtim's last years in prison coincided with the time when we were waiting for the sick dictator to die. Kujtim, now in his fourth decade of his sentence, was exhausted. You could tell this from his clothes, which he had previously kept clean, however worn they were, but were now spotted with stains.

Rumours that the dictator was nearing the end of his life had been circulating in prison for some time, nourishing hopes that his death would change our own fortunes. Kujtim said that he felt himself in a race with him. Which would survive the other? He was afraid that, even if he was still alive when his sentence was finished, they wouldn't release him while the dictator was still alive, but would give him more years. What worried him about this race was not that, if he died first, he wouldn't live to see the death of this hated figure, nor that he wouldn't go home to live with his relatives, but that his poems would remain buried in his own brain.

Despite every effort to make the dictator look as healthy as possible when he appeared in public, one look at him showed that the rumours were not without substance. His public appearances became rarer. Then, whenever he was present, the camera would catch him looking abstracted and remote, however the operator tried to avoid it.

Kujtim would look out for him on television whenever the dictator appeared at the usual events he had never missed, the First of May, the anniversary of the Liberation, and important meetings that he couldn't fail to attend. Kujtim sought signs of his imminent demise in his every gesture, his trembling hands, and his evident loss of concentration. He was heartened when he saw these symptoms and cast into despair when he didn't. One day he came to me and said that he was writing a poem about this anxious waiting but he had abandoned it half way because of two lines that wouldn't fit:

> The criminal's face, now pale, now bright
> Appears like the moon in the sky at night.

'You can't compare this criminal to the moon,' he said, 'and I don't know why it turned out like that, but it wasn't just because of the rhyme.'

The dictator died a few months later. Kujtim was relieved of a great burden and his health also improved. He became more confident that he would come out of prison alive.

* * *

The day of his release came, with Kujtim entering his thirty-third year in prison.

When Kujtim arrived in the anteroom to be searched for the last time, the young officer assigned to open the gate held a release order that he had to read twice, one time to check that this broken old man was the person who according to the document was not yet fifty, and another time to grasp the fact that he had entered prison at fifteen, and instead of the schoolroom and playground, had been brought up in prison cells and forced labour camps, and not by parents and teachers, but by investigators, guards, and prisoners.

The guard carrying out the search took out from Kujtim's bag a thick notebook of the kind that prisoners fashioned in Burrel by sewing together the spines of several notebooks and binding them in thick boards made by gluing sheets of paper and surgical gauze with macaroni paste. The young officer picked up this book and saw written on the front in beautiful capital letters, *The Tragedies of Sophocles*. Then he opened the book and read the words that Kujtim had written inside:

Anyone who lives by poetry knows that in pain a voice always sounds the same as in joy.

The tones of this voice are a question of form, and its subjects a matter of time and place.

In these glorious pages, any person can find their own self and their own fragile destiny.

The young officer stood for a few moments in hesitation, not knowing whether to let this book through or confiscate it. Kujtim explained that this was a translation he'd made in Burrel prison. They had allowed him to translate it there and take it with him, because Sophocles wasn't a forbidden writer. The officer was slightly surprised to hear Kujtim's voice, because he had expected it to be as feeble as this man appeared, but it was clear and assertive. He pondered a moment, and then stretched out his hand with the notebook for Kujtim to put it in his bag.

But when he opened the gate and let Kujtim pass, he couldn't know that he had let through something else that his search hadn't found, something he couldn't find or even imagine. The still active brain of this former prisoner who seemed at the end of his life contained several volumes of poems, preserved there and nowhere else.

These were the sole possessions and the sole meaning of the life of this man whose passion, since the age of fifteen, had been for reckless heroes and for knowledge.

Zef Mala

I had been fond of the word *kaush* since childhood. It reminded me of primary school, where peddlers used to come to us in the yard during the long break to sell us those paper cones called *kaushë* filled brimful with the sweet black hackberries that grew in the gardens of Tirana.

We not only enjoyed eating the hackberries, but they brought us together because the berries of one *kaush* would be shared out among several of us. Then we used the hackberry stones as 'bullets' in our war games. We would load them into the barrels of our 'pistols', which were pieces of reed that we always kept in our pockets, and blow these 'bullets' at each other.

These memories of childhood meant that I never entirely got used to the meaning of the word *kaush* in prison slang.

* * *

I heard this word on my first day when, after being sentenced by the court, I was taken down from the solitary cells of the investigator's office to this place strangely known as the *kaush*. It was a section of the ground floor of Tirana prison where the Directorate of Prisons gathered all the recently convicted prisoners from throughout the country for allocation to the different camps and prisons. Longstanding prisoners were also brought there for transfer from one camp to another, and when they were sent to the prison hospital or summoned to court proceedings in Tirana.

The *kaush* was a transit point through which every prisoner passed at least once in his life. The language of the Directorate of Prisons no doubt had a term for it, most probably a section number of Department 313, as Tirana Prison was called.

Over the years I noticed that there were many words in prison slang that I had never heard before, which were born out of a need to describe the special features of this world. Some of them were constructed from words used in life outside, which acquired a new meaning. Some of them were created by joining words from life outside into new phrases. Other words were entirely original. Living in that world, you could see how the prisoners' own creativity had enriched their slang. Someone would give a new meaning to a familiar word which would then be taken up and passed on by others. The most well-known example was 'meat' which was used for new deliveries of prisoners by the prison van. But there were also expressions devised by the guards, such as the word 'nest' for a punishment cell, attributed to the malicious Pjetër Koka.

We learned prison slang and used it instinctively, and as time passed it became our first language. So few of us could ever again use the word *kaush* to denote the paper cone in which the peddlers sold hackberries, mulberries, jujubes and roasted chestnuts. For a long time, I felt sure that this new meaning had been thought up by some prisoners without much sensitivity to childhood memories, seeing how prisoners were crammed into this *kaush* like hackberries in a paper cone.

It was five years before I met someone who knew more about the word and I discovered that like many other slang words its origins lay deeper in the past. And I found this out in the *kaush* itself.

* * *

'Zef Mala is up there on the third level, very ill.' This was the first thing I heard as soon as I entered the *kaush*, before I had sorted out my belongings. I had arrived there from Spaç after an exhausting journey in the prison van, together with a group of prisoners who had created problems in the camp. After our punishments in isolation, they had decided finally to transfer us.

As I was arranging the place where I was to sleep, I couldn't rid my mind of this news: the name of Zef Mala was familiar to me, part of the history of the Communist Party that every child learned at school. This history included certain culminating points, important battles in the National Liberation War and the upheavals of the revolution and socialist construction. The history of this struggle mentioned the names of 'enemies' and 'groups hostile to the Party' who had tried to divert or obstruct the course of the revolution and the building of socialism. Even at Party congresses that were broadcast far and wide, the dictator would start his speeches by recalling the historic victories over these enemies. The list of enemies grew longer from one congress to the next, but was always headed by Zef Mala.

He had been the chairman of the communist group in the city of Shkodër who was accused, for personal ambition, of opposing the creation of a joint communist party and maintaining an opportunistic, social-democratic attitude to the revolution.

The history textbooks didn't mention what had happened subsequently to Zef. The stories of these enemies ended at the moment of their ideological elimination. They vanished from the pages of the book, just as they disappeared from public life, and any further existence they might have was meaningless; whether they managed to escape the country, were killed and buried with or without trial, ended up in prison or internment, or were left in freedom in some remote corner of the country.

The fact that Zef was alive and under the same roof as myself aroused my curiosity. To encounter a person like this was like meeting the ghost of someone who died long ago, who had indeed died many times over. I could hardly wait to meet and talk to him. But I had an additional reason to meet him, because I was indirectly associated with this list of adversaries, for my father was among the old communists whom the dictator had declared to be enemies during his later purges.

* * *

It wasn't easy to choose a place to sleep in the *kaush* because each of the three levels had its advantages and drawbacks. The favourite places were the corners of whatever floor, because you wouldn't have any other person on one side of you, but these were all taken. The third level was preferable because there was more light: the window grilles were at the top, and you didn't have anybody above with their dust falling on you, and you weren't open to the gaze of people walking in the corridor. But the drawback was that all the tobacco smoke and stench of the *kaush* gathered there, and there were light bulbs above your head that were never turned off.

The youngest generally chose the third level because you had to climb there on wooden ladders that were fixed every two or three metres at the end of the platforms. Anybody who would rather have more oxygen and less light at night had to sleep below, but at the cost of more dust. The person you would sleep next to also influenced your choice, because a place near someone you knew was preferable to one among strangers.

I finally chose a place on the second level in the middle of the platform alongside two others who had recently arrived with me from Spaç. After I made my bed, I lay back to rest a little, watching the comings and goings of the prisoners in the corridor between the end of the platform and the outer wall of the *kaush*.

The corridor was very lively. The *kaush* was also a place of reunions and new acquaintanceships, especially between newly convicted prisoners and veterans. The youngest and most vigorous prisoners exchanged information below in the corridor. Others sat in twos and threes on the beds on the platforms, smoking and chatting. The most visible signs of a new prisoner were a pale face, having being deprived of the sun for months in the investigators' cells, along with the clothes from civilian life which they wore until they were sent to a camp. The veteran prisoners were recognisable immediately by the faded clothes from the administration and the caps made in the camp from scraps of fabric.

The newly sentenced prisoners were keen to meet people and find out what was happening in the camps and prisons where they would spend the years to come, and the veterans were thirsty for information about what was happening in life outside.

* * *

After about an hour an elderly prisoner came down from the third floor and nudged me out of the doze I had fallen into after my tiring journey. He introduced himself as Jaku, an old friend of Zef, who was also looking after him. The two had been together in Ballsh, but he himself would now be transferred. He expected to be sent to Spaç or Burrel prison.

'Zef likes to meet you children of old communists,' he said with a smile that struck me as slightly ironic, 'Because sometimes he knew your fathers from the time of the anti-fascist struggle.'

There were some others in the *kaush* like myself, the sons of enemies on the list, who had been sentenced and sentenced again because the dictator had said in a speech that the sons of enemies posed a danger. I understood that Jaku's irony stemmed from the fact that members of our fathers' generation, some out of blind faith in the dictator and others in the hope that their turn to be bitten by him would never come, had never once raised their voices against this list until one day they found themselves on it. As I thought about my meeting with Zef, I couldn't fail to have my hesitations, because who knew what he thought about these people.

'Of course,' I said. 'So he's also met the others here in the *kaush*?'

'Yes, yes.'

Before we climbed to the next level, I asked Jaku how Zef's health was. Jaku told me he had been discharged from the prison hospital and brought to the *kaush* to be sent back to the camp of Ballsh, probably because his case was hopeless: lung cancer. 'He's not well at all,' Jaku added. 'I'm afraid he won't last long.'

I thought that Zef must have chosen the third level to be more secluded, but Jaku explained to me that it was because there was more light. An untreated, deteriorating glaucoma had left him almost blind.

'And up there it's warmer,' he said. 'Because he's very thin and he feels the cold.'

My imagined meeting with the ghost of a man who had died several times turned out not to be far from reality after I climbed the steps. I knew that Zef must be just over sixty, but with his quenched eyes beneath two heavy, luxuriant, grey eyebrows which blocked almost his entire field of vision, he looked at least ten years older. I understood that this appearance was not a result of lack of care, but because he barely needed his eyes any more. It was also clear that it was other problems, more serious than loss of vision, that had reduced him to this state of skin and bone.

And so I was astonished when he greeted me in a voice still full of life that conveyed a desire to communicate. For the first time it struck me that the voice is a person's last characteristic to show the effects of age.

Firstly, we talked about his health.

'Either an old tubercular problem has come back, which is not a problem, because it will pass with antibiotics, or I have cancer, in which case I'll die,' he said.

The calm with which he pronounced these words left behind a silence that only he could break, and so I waited for what he would say next.

'But I believe in the vitalist theory,' he went on, without completing his sentence because he was seized by a hacking cough. He covered his mouth with a handkerchief, coughed for a while, and settled down.

'According to this theory,' he continued, 'every person is given a portion of life to use up, like fuel. This gets consumed, depending on what he does with it. As far as I can make out, I've run through my share.'

Jaku tried to make a joke of this, to cheer him up, saying that he had filled his entire petrol tank with information.

'And by reading books,' he said, turning to me. 'When they took us for transfer, we were reading *Don Quixote* together, his favourite book. Do you remember that, Zef?'

Zef nodded.

'We'll take it up where we left off. I think it was at the letter that Don Quixote sends to Sancho as the governor of Barataria, because Zef too,' he said, 'sent a letter with advice to the ruler. He wrote, 'To win the love of the people, Sancho, you should remember two things: to be generous to everyone and to make sure there's plenty of food.' Ha-ha-ha. 'And don't forget, if you're judging some unfortunate character who's committed a crime and you're not sure of his punishment, err on the side of clemency.' And the governor, to thank him for the advice, showed clemency and slapped another ten years on his sentence.'

Zef tried to laugh, but his cough seized him again. When he recovered, he took from his pocket a packet of *Partizan* and with trembling fingers extracted a cigarette and placed it in his mouth with a mechanical movement, evidently a lifelong habit. Jaku lit it for him.

He coughed heavily after the first drag and this prevented him from talking any more. Then he pulled on his cigarette again and cast a silent look in my direction. I couldn't make out what his weary, grey eyes could see of my face. Jaku knew that Zef couldn't do two things at once, and so began talking in his place.

'This man is the only political prisoner who has been imprisoned and interned under all three regimes in the history of the Albanian state. He was in prison in the time of the king. He was in prison under fascism. He's been in prison twice under communism. And the irony is that all these sentences are linked to one other. The second couldn't have come without the first, the third couldn't have happened without the first and second, and nor the fourth without the three before. Under the king he was sentenced for ten years as a communist. When the fascists came, they interned him on the island of Ventotene. There he met Spinelli, Pertini, and many other Italian socialists. He changed his mind about Stalinism and became a libertarian socialist. In the summer of 1943, when Mussolini fell, he was released and he came back to Albania. He tried to persuade our communists that Stalin was an enemy of freedom, and that Albania's future must be with Spinelli's united Europe. They declared him an enemy of the party. He was spared a medal by a miracle.'

'A medal?' I turned to Jaku with wide eyes.

'Don't you know what the dictator meant by a 'medal' during the war?'

'No.'

'The dictator often sent letters with instructions to the party's people who operated in the towns. When there was someone who had to be liquidated, he would write, 'give him a medal.' This was the order for Zef too, but they changed their mind. It seems that an old comrade of his from the communist group in Shkodër used his influence to prevent them killing him. Nevertheless, as soon as the war was over, they threw him inside. And so Zef continued with the prisons of communism, which made the king's prison and his internment on Ventotene seem like paradise.'

Zef listened attentively without interrupting even when he had finished his cigarette. I was thinking how some people suffer all the misfortunes of the epochs in which they live. As if he were reading my mind, he spoke up in his firm voice:

'These things that Jaku is describing aren't misfortunes. They are the consequences of the choices I've made.'

He wanted to say more about this, but coughing overcame him again and I remained silent a while, waiting for him to settle down.

'But do you have any family?' I asked when I saw he was calm.

'I was married during the war. My wife was a communist. Our two daughters were born just after the war. Then they put me in prison. After my first sentence, I saw that my name was a burden for both my wife and the children, so we divorced. They divorced me. I haven't seen them since. But I don't set much store by blood relatives. I value intellectual and spiritual friendship much more. When I was interned, I married another wife, from the village, who has never left me.

At that point in the conversation the guard opened the door of the *kaush*.

'*Pa-jto-s*,' he shouted, lengthening the vowels: 'Fresh air.'

* * *

The word *pajtos* was also one of the first words I learned in prison, but unlike *kaush*, I had never heard it used in life outside. It had two meanings: going outside for the one hour of fresh air, and the area where this took place.

Zef wanted to come out with us. Jaku helped him descend the steps, bearing almost his whole weight. We hurried out into the rectangular yard surrounded by high walls and topped with barbed wire. It was very cold, with a biting wind. The soldier in the watchtower at the corner of the yard where the two perimeter walls joined marched on the spot to keep warm.

On the opposite wall, we were faced with a quotation from the dictator, 'The slogans of our enemies are merely their wail of defeat.' It had been there for some time, but it seemed to have been renewed with a fresh coat of red paint.

The prisoners began to walk briskly round the icy cement of the exercise yard. Jaku and I, escorting Zef, followed him at his slow pace. Sometimes I couldn't fail to turn my head towards the slogan. I had never seen it displayed when I was free. Obviously it had been chosen from the dictator's books especially for the prison wall, as a response to the insults and curses we let fly among ourselves, as if to tell us not to harbour any illusion that in those moments we were free, or that we were any different from those outside, who did not dare to curse, because with all our vituperation we were only bewailing our own defeat.

Zefi was unable to read this, and in his present state there was no point in asking him what he thought. We young people who hoped to see the dictator dead one day might endure this slogan, but not Zef. He moved more and more slowly, leaning ever more heavily on Jaku's arms. Soon the December cold irritated his lungs, and he could not stop coughing. He stood stock still, giving us to understand that he could walk no further. We took him by the arms, led him into the *kaush*, and helped him back up to the third level. As soon as he calmed down, he asked for a cigarette, but we told him to rest. He buried his head in the blankets and seemed to fall asleep.

* * *

When I was left alone with Jaku, he told me about Zef's life under communism. After his first prison sentence he went back to Tirana, where he was overlooked for a few years because this was the time when the dictator broke with the Soviets and the principal enemies had become the Khrushchevite revisionists, especially the specialists who had studied in the Soviet Union. But he never forgot his old enemies. Zef had an ordinary job in Tirana as a bookkeeper and he didn't bother anybody, but a chance encounter with the dictator, at a distance, led to him being interned.

One sunny winter afternoon Zef had gone out for a walk on the Tirana boulevard. To his misfortune he happened to walk along the pavement opposite the Central Committee building at the very moment when the dictator was watching passers-by from the window of his office. This was a moment when he savoured his power. He seemed to himself like God, watching everybody from above and deciding their fate. Depending on his mood, he would sometimes watch with the feeling of a shepherd for his flock, or try to find someone familiar in the midst of this flock, and sometimes he would eye these pedestrians with the suspicion that there might be an enemy among them.

On that day his attention was drawn by a solitary man with a derby hat walking slowly along the opposite pavement. Who was this man who dared to wear a derby? There was no law against such a thing, but people had gradually, over the years, come to realise that there was a hierarchy to headgear. The common sort did best to remain bareheaded. Then came caps, which were a sign of revolutionary proletarians or secretaries of low-level party organisations. But a derby was something special. In fact, it was the sign of a bourgeois or a gentleman, unsuitable for the new man of socialism, and yet paradoxically it was also a distinguishing feature of the leadership.

Indeed, it was the main visible sign of their high status, especially that of the dictator. It was as if the derby showed that only they were immune from bourgeois thinking, or that they were the sole remaining gentlemen in the country. After all, people needed signs of some sort to distinguish their leaders from the rest.

At the time of the Chinese cultural revolution, the dictator had worn a particular cap in the style of Mao Zedong, but before long he went back to the derby, a white one in summer, and a dark fabric one in winter. Indeed, photos of him with a derby in his right hand, waving at the crowd of demonstrators from the rostrum on 1st May, were among the most common.

Had it not been for the derby, the dictator might not have recognised Zef, because one solitary man wouldn't have caught his eye. But when after pondering the matter, he came to the conclusion that Zef had appeared dressed like that because he suspected that the dictator's power was approaching its end, and his temper was roused.

The *Sigurimi* chiefs were forced into self-criticism for leaving such a dangerous enemy at large in the capital.

A few days later, the internment order came for Zef. Usually enemies originating from the north were sent to the south, and the other way round, but never anywhere near the border. They sent Zef, as a northerner, to a remote village in the south. Some time later, he wrote from there the letter which became the reason that he was arrested again and sentenced to ten years for agitation and propaganda.

* * *

In the evening, soup was brought in a cauldron and distributed by ladle at the entrance to the *kaush*. About an hour later, the door was opened for a last toilet trip. Jaku carefully helped Zef to climb down. When they were returning, our paths crossed in the corridor and Zef told me that they would wait for me up above to finish the conversation.

After supper was the best time for talk. Most of the prisoners gathered in groups round the beds of those leading the conversation and stayed up till late.

'What did you write in that letter that upset him badly enough to have you arrested?' I asked Zef when I had climbed up to his level.

'In internment, I suffered even more than in my first prison sentence, because in internment you are neither free nor imprisoned and you are much more lonely than in prison. I had only my wife there. If it had been up to me, I would have written that letter earlier, but my wife said to me, "Don't!" But I couldn't put up with it any longer. Now I feel sorry for her.'

'But what did you write?'

'The things I had seen and still saw around me. As the socialist I am I ended by saying that there is no freedom without socialism, but there can also be no socialism without freedom. A few days later they came for me with handcuffs. Now here I am in the *kaush*. Do you know why they call this place where we are the *kaush*?'

'No,' I said, 'and I'm curious to know.'

'If you're interested in the language of prison, you'll find no better expert than me because I've been in prison under three regimes.'

'Why do you say language and not slang?' I asked, pricking up my ears to listen.

'Because slang is the language invented by the prisoners, but the words that the guards use too are a part of the Albanian language, describing the prison. They're like the words to describe cars, which we've borrowed from the languages of those who have brought us cars. For instance, we've taken *motore*, *carrozzeria* and *cofano* from Italian. During my first sentence, I remember that the majority of words about prison came from Ottoman Turkish: we called the prison itself *hapsanë* more often than *burg* which is a word used for castles in the West. Then Slavic words came in during my second spell in prison.'

'Is that so?' I exclaimed, for this sort of etymology had never occurred to my mind.

'Do you know where the word *pendrek* comes from?'

'No.'

'It's what they call a truncheon in Serbo-Croatian.'

'So what about *pajtos*?' I asked, my curiosity roused.

'It's written *pajdos*, not *pajtos*. This is also an Ottoman word that perhaps they took from the Greeks. When I was a child, I remember it was used for breaktime at school, or the lunch hour for people who worked in the afternoon. But it's also used in the sense of ceasefire. Now it survives only as the hour of fresh air in prisons, like a kind of ceasefire in the war against evil that we fight in the cells.'

'So where does the word *kaush* come from?'

'This comes from Ottoman Turkish too. *Kavuşmak* means to gather. And they have gathered us here.'

'Like hackberries in the paper cones we had as children?'

'Exactly. But I remember an old prisoner during my first sentence, who had done time in prison under the Ottoman Empire. He said that they also used *kaush* for a kind of punishment cell, where they put the most dangerous prisoners. It was like a well, in the shape of a cone. The prisoners couldn't lie down because of the floor narrowed to a point, and they couldn't walk, so they were forced to remain on their feet. I don't know if cells like that really existed, I don't believe they did, but this story has stuck in my mind because I think of my life as always spent in a cone like that.'

He attempted to laugh when he said that, but his cough returned. I waited for it to stop, but it turned into an endless fit. Jaku changed the cloth that he put to his mouth when he coughed, noticing that it was stained with blood.

I caught Jaku's eye and understood that Zef had talked for a long time and I should leave him in peace. I said good night and climbed down the steps to my bed to sleep, thinking that perhaps the next day I might find the moment to ask him what he thought about the list of enemies, headed by his own name, and if he felt any consolation because those who followed him had each been complicit in the arrest of their predecessors, whereas he had not.

* * *

But the following morning, I had just finished tea when the door opened and I was summoned by name with several other prisoners. We had to gather our clothes quickly because the prison van was waiting to take us to the camp at Ballsh.

I got ready and said goodbye to the prisoners who were left in the *kaush*, and climbed above for a moment to bid farewell to Zef. He was shrouded in blankets from head to foot. He raised his head and I told him I was leaving, but we would meet again soon in Ballsh. He reached out to me without a word and held my hand tightly for a few moments.

I climbed down the steps, with that handshake burning my palm, a farewell that I didn't want to accept.

* * *

One week later, the prison van arrived again in Ballsh with new prisoners from the *kaush*. They brought the news that Zef had died.

I remembered his handshake. I had clasped his hand to mine as a temporary parting, but now I had to accept it as a final farewell. Then I recalled the moments of my meeting with him: his vitalist theory of the portion of life he had used up, the story of the derby hat that Jaku had told me, his letter to the dictator saying there is no freedom without socialism, but no socialism without freedom, and my regret that I never asked him what he thought of the long list of our fathers who were declared enemies, with his own name at the top, and finally our conversation about the *kaush* as a cone-shaped cell.

And then I imagined his grave like a cone of this kind, in which he couldn't lie down to rest in peace, even in death.

Çuçi

'There's light!' I exclaimed as soon as soon as I entered Cell No. 4 of Burrel prison, before saying hello to anyone.

The light struck me as soon as the guard opened the door. There were eight or nine other inmates in the cell, but I was taken aback by this bright natural light. In the camps, I'd known many people who had come from Burrel prison, and some had served several stints there, and yet my mental picture of the place had stayed almost the same as when I was in freedom. It was the archetypal conception of a prison – a place of darkness, with tiny grilles, half underground – a picture formed in childhood, which had survived the test of reality and remained untouched somewhere in a backwater of my imagination.

One prisoner, I forget who, laughed at my remark, and said that I had come at a time of year when the sun struck the southern wall where the bars were, and on a bright day. Nevertheless, I had certainly imagined the grilles would be much smaller.

* * *

The prisoners squatted on pallets in rows on a plank platform set against one wall, about half a metre off the floor. I greeted them in turn. It was a pleasant surprise to find that every face was familiar: almost all of them were former prisoners of Spaç, brought here for second sentences. Bardhi was in the far corner, under the grille. He hadn't changed much in the years since we last saw each other. He was smoking a pipe, and my pleasure at meeting him again was spoiled only by the immediate thought of how all this smoke would irritate me.

After Bardhi came Nikolla, who had also been given a second sentence in Spaç. He stood up from where he had been squatting with a book between his legs and hugged me. My pallet would be next to Nikolla's. Then came Pupi with a roll-up in his mouth, his hands busy sticking together the cardboard from which prisoners made little boxes to hold photographs and oddments. He offered me his hand and grasped mine firmly. After Pupi came Nuredin. It was particularly moving to meet him again, for he had turned very grey. After Nuredin came Qani, who had aged more than any of us, and was unrecognisable. I said how surprised I was to see him like this, and he told me about his stomach trouble. In the other corner by the door was Kërluku, of whom I'd heard that he could flare up and quarrel with anybody over a word out of place. But he also had his good-natured side, and he embraced me warmly.

Opposite the platform were two beds along the wall of the cell, divided from ours by a very narrow aisle. Pëto slept in one of these. His name was Shpëtim, but people called him Pëto. He was the only one who hadn't come from Spaç. He told me that he'd arrived from the camp for ordinary criminals at Saranda, where they had sentenced him for trying to escape to Greece. He was the youngest in the room and was knitting socks or a jumper of some kind on two wooden needles. Stavri, whom we called Çavo, slept in the corner. He worked as the cleaner on this wing. He was so thin that I failed to recognise him at first. 'Where have I seen this person before?' I asked myself. When he spoke and I heard the Greek accent, I remembered Çavo. He helped carry my belongings into the room.

It was an important day in Burrel when new prisoners were brought from the camp, an event that took place only every few months, and sometimes only once in several years. Newcomers were welcomed, told how different they looked, and then bombarded with questions about the political gossip, and what was happening out there in the camp. The prisoners asked about relatives and filled in each other's life-stories for the periods since they'd last met.

I looked in vain for the packet of filter cigarettes I had brought to hand round, as the custom was. It must have been stolen from me during the search at the gate.

*　*　*

Later that afternoon I discovered the other occupant of our room. This was Çuçi, Çavo's cat, and also the pet of the whole cell. She was a cat with black and white patches, but with more black on her back and more white on her belly, chest, and throat. She was a pretty cat with a white tail that she held vertically and twitched slightly as she walked, and a fine head with one green eye shot with black markings and the other with white.

Çuçi entered together with Çavo, who had finished his cleaning duty. She followed him to his bed and began to rub against him while he prepared food for her. He took a small fish from a tin, mixed it with some crumbs of bread, and gave this to her. Çuçi devoured it at once, licked her lips, and then went to Qani's bed, where she was given a little cheese. Çavo told me that Çuçi was about two years old and that he'd brought her up since she was a kitten. Yet not many prisoners formed attachments to cats, compared to the indifferent majority. These men came from a society where cats were kept as mousers, and fed on scraps or left to fend for themselves, so for most of those who became fond of cats this was their first love of this kind. Of course, these attachments were also an expression of frustrated fatherly feelings, but prisoners generally became more attached to female cats than tom-cats, suggesting that they met to some extent the need for a woman's love, and became part children, part lovers.

It was hard to tell whether the love for these animals was a projection of paternal love mixed with confused sexual instincts, or a special kind of affection that one can only feel for animals. Cats were different to both children and lovers, in their silence, their lack of aggression, and the pleasure and inner peace they brought when you stroked their soft fur.

In the camps, most of the prisoners who kept cats did not keep them close to themselves. The cats wandered through the yards, ran off, mated wherever they wanted, and were in a much wilder state than Çuçi. But she too was free to make love to the tom-cats of Burrel prison, and once had given birth to two kittens. They had not lived, and it's said that kittens from a first pregnancy never survive. But Çuçi also spent hours on end in the cell with us, even during the night. Almost every evening, she came back to the cell after wandering through the yards and hidden corners of the prison. She squeezed in through the observation window in the door, an opening fifteen centimetres square at the level of the human eye, which the guards always left open.

The window was divided down the middle by an iron bar that Çavo had bent slightly to enlarge one of the gaps. Çuçi would scramble up the outside of the door, put her head through the larger gap, followed by her body, and then launch herself – thwup – into the room. Sometimes she came late, after we'd fallen asleep. She had a habit of burrowing under the blankets of each prisoner, one after another.

We hadn't felt anything like her soft touch for so long. It wasn't the touch of a woman, but only an animal, yet we felt warmed by another creature, with the intimacy this brings. This pleasure was very strong in this society of men, where contact with any other body, in other words the body of a man, was taboo. Whenever Çuçi came to burrow under my blankets, I was careful not to disturb her, so that she would stay as long as possible.

Çavo wasn't jealous of her closeness to other prisoners. Çuçi indeed wandered freely, stopping to rub herself against each one of us, but when we went out for fresh air, it was only Çavo's shoulder that she chose to jump on. When we were in the room, she would sit only on his chest, staring at his eyes in curiosity and rubbing her head against his chin. Çavo knew that Çuçi would come to him at once when he called her. Only once did Çavo quarrel over Çuçi with a prisoner from Cell No. 3. This prisoner had plenty of food from his family, and apparently was using titbits to tempt the lovely Çuçi away from him. The story ended with a fist-fight in the yard, and both the prisoners were sentenced to the punishment cells.

* * *

I had met Çavo for the first time in Spaç in '75. He was then a young man of twenty-two, from the Greek minority in Derviçan, and had ended up in prison because of an attempted escape. He was sentenced to only four years and released shortly afterwards, but before two years had passed he was back in Spaç, again for trying to escape. He had set off from Derviçan on a snowy winter's night, thinking that this was the best time to cross into Greece, but had fallen into a pit somewhere in the mountains near the border and hadn't been able to pull himself out by dawn. He was found and caught the next morning. This time he got twenty years.

He was very thin when he came to Spaç, but he soon filled out. His family brought him plenty of parcels. Besides, he had a strong stomach that could digest anything. He even ate raw cabbage, which came to the camp in large quantities to be turned into soup. We were surprised to see how soon he grew stout and ruddy. Because he was young and powerfully built, they gave him a job as a mallet-man in Zone Three. Çavo was one of the few with such a strong spirit of resistance, or such a poor ability to reconcile himself to misfortune, that he was ready to risk death itself in order to challenge it.

What made Çavo different from a thousand others who had submitted to their fate? It wasn't his calculation that twenty years of forced labour would leave him with blackened lungs even if he didn't perish in some mine accident. Sober calculation would tell him to resign himself, because he had very little chance of escaping alive through the two high barbed wire fences of Spaç, illuminated at night with lamps fixed on the supporting posts, and with a watchtower every hundred metres where a soldier with a machine gun turned a searchlight 360 degrees over the entire area. Even if he did manage to get beyond the camp boundary, as had happened in a few rare cases, everybody knew that nobody had got through the fortifications on the state border in the last twenty or thirty years. The regime mobilised the entire population to catch fugitives. It was the combination of a passionate desire to fly away to freedom and an extraordinary lack of fear of death that distinguished Çavo from the rest of us, who heeded the voice of reason, listened to the stories of failed escapes, and feared death.

So, one day towards the end of November or the beginning of December 1977, barely a few months after he had arrived, he escaped with Manoli, one of his wagon-pushers, who also came from the Greek minority. They scrambled down the stream bed that passed through a spot where the searchlights shed a poor light, slipped under the perimeter wire and ran out on the other side. A soldier in the watch tower was sentenced to two years for negligence, and people said that he told the court that he had seen something move, but thought it was an animal.

After three days' search, the two prisoners were captured somewhere in the forests of Puka. In fact, they were forced to surrender or perish because they were caught in a snowstorm and a gale, and had nothing to eat. Winter snow was Çavo's undoing twice in one year.

Commissar Shahin called a meeting a few days later, and said to us, 'You'll see the back of Stavri Guxo.' The mention of his name but not Manoli's suggested that their punishments would differ, and not just by the number of years. The court indeed sentenced Çavo to death as a third-time offender, and the sentence would have been carried out if Enver Hoxha had not by coincidence visited Gjirokastra and made a speech about the state's good treatment of the Greek minority. Shooting a young man of the Greek minority only because he wanted to escape abroad would not go unreported in Greece, and would be in flagrant contradiction to this policy. But from now on it was unthinkable that Çavo would see out his sentence anywhere but in Burrel prison.

* * *

Çavo had now served ten years and had aged so much that I barely recognised him. He was hardworking and honest, and had recently been assigned as a cleaner. His task was to mop the long corridor, down one side of which ran the row of cells, and also the corridor of the punishment cells, and then to sweep the exercise yard, scrub the lavatories, and light the coal-fired boiler that provided us with showers every ten days. It was not tiring work, and he had the privilege of staying out in the exercise yard with the prisoners of all the cells from that wing. Nevertheless, this work often irritated Çavo because some of the guards got on his nerves. One day, after quarrelling with a guard who had asked him to clean his duty-room and light his fire, he told his cellmates that he wanted to give up his job. 'But what would I do with this creature?' he added, pointing to Çuçi, who was waiting for him to prepare some breadcrumbs and cheese. He never let her out of his sight.

* * *

Çuçi was on good terms with all of us, though not everybody liked her equally. After Çavo, Qani and Pupi loved her most. Qani expressed his affection by feeding her more than anyone else. He was a kind man, unaffected and full of jokes, but he had fared very badly in prison. He had arrived in Spaç with a sentence of only six years, but, because of his candid nature, he fell a prey to the spies, so that one fine day he was taken away and sentenced to a further ten. Moreover, he was sent back to Spaç and put down the mine again. There he reached for an adze and attacked one of the spies who had denounced him and stood witness against him. He struck him on the head with all his strength, but without killing him, and this saved his own life too. He was sentenced to a further twenty-five years and sent back to Burrel. Here he developed stomach ulcers, and often threw up everything that he ate.

Although he needed a special diet, he couldn't bear not sharing with Çuçi the delicacies that he bought in the shop. We would only leave for Çuçi the skins of the small amounts of salami that we bought, but he almost always went halves with her. He gave her cheese, of which Çuçi was very fond, and sardines, to the point of annoying Çavo, who did not want her to become used to eating without bread.

Pupi didn't find it easy to express his feelings. His life had been extremely difficult. When he was small, he had been put in the children's re-education home. He was one of 'Makarenko's lot', as Qani laughingly said, and you could tell he'd been deprived of affection. He had a firm character with special talents, particularly for painting. Over the years, he had brooded on the bitter experiences that life had dealt him and constructed his own philosophy of life, which was to preserve honour and dignity, even in the most wretched circumstances.

'I get along fine, if you remember the shit I came out of,' was his reply when anybody teased him for gobbling noisily as he ate. Pupi did not often stroke Çuçi, but when her first two kittens miscarried, it was his strong fingers that pulled out the second of the litter. Otherwise Çuçi would have died.

Bardhosh enjoyed talking to Çuçi more than stroking her. He often commented on her cunning and duplicity when she came up to him for the tastiest treat.

Nuredin fed her regularly and continually stroked her, and Nikolla, who spent all his time hunched over a thick notebook into which he was copying a manuscript of the whole of Dante's *Inferno*, passed down from previous prisoners of Burrel, would stop writing whenever Çuçi appeared and stroke her. Pëto was not so attached to her.

Despite our affection for Çuçi, it did not occur to any of us to keep her indoors. Whenever she became bored in the room, she would leave through one of the windows. From there she would throw herself into the back yard of the prison and cross into the commander's yard. She could even go into the town if she wished, and would return, passing from one yard to the next through the drainage culverts.

She was well fed but her hunting instinct was still very strong. Her mother too had apparently been a good hunter. The guards kept rabbits somewhere in the commander's yard, and these rabbits were Cuci's favourite prey. We couldn't see into this yard, but Çuçi used to visit it. When rabbits were being born, she visited us more rarely, and seemed to quiver when she entered the room. She would suddenly freeze with ears erect and all at once hurl herself at the window frame, scuttling off into the governor's yard. You could tell if she had feasted off a young rabbit: when she came back, her white throat would be stained with blood.

We felt no pity for the commander's rabbits. On the contrary, we were glad that Çuçi was such a fine hunter, and we had still less sympathy for the rabbit breeders. But one day after roll-call, Kosta the prison commissar said to Çavo, before the duty guard closed the door, 'Stavro, I will kill that cat. It eats our rabbits.'

Çavo muttered a denial that Çuçi would do such a thing.

We considered Kosta the commissar a decent, lackadaisical sort, and quickly forgot what he said.

*　*　*

Çavo was not the sort to share his deepest fears and worries. He was a man of action and few words. He had prepared his escape from Spaç in the deepest secrecy, confiding only in Manoli. So we couldn't imagine that he could be so terror-struck at the thought that they might kill Çuçi. Yet he made no attempt to stop her going into the back yard of the prison, from where she would set off in search of rabbits.

One afternoon, when we were all sitting on our pallets, minding our own business, we heard a rifle shot. We would have overlooked it, because many shots came from that direction, but Çavo said at once:

'They've killed Çuçi.'

We paid little attention to him. Nevertheless, that supper time we waited for Çuçi more anxiously than usual. She did not come. This had happened before. We waited for her the next evening and the next, and still Çuçi did not come. Whenever we raised the subject, Çavo said, 'No doubt about it. They've killed her.' Yet we felt that deep down he still kept hoping, and this superficial certainty was his way of preparing for the worst.

Meanwhile, Qani suggested that maybe they hadn't killed her. Perhaps one of the officers who was fond of her had taken her away, because she was a pretty cat, or because he had a problem with mice and knew she was a good hunter. And so the days passed in increasing anxiety over Çuçi's failure to return, until the incident with Velo.

Velo was a young guard, tall, and with a slightly womanly build, that is a broad behind and narrow shoulders. However, he was as sadistic as he was effeminate. His sadism was not expressed directly by taking pleasure in beatings. It was Shukja who was famous for that, one of the most brutal guards at Burrel, who was often Velo's mate on his shift. Shukja had come from a camp for ordinary criminals, with the reputation of beating prisoners in two ways: he would take a very recalcitrant prisoner, make him lie prone, cover him with a piece of sheet metal and beat him as hard as he could. His other method, with the less resistant, was to take the prisoner to the tool store and ask him to choose the shaft of a spade or a pickaxe, whichever he preferred for a beating.

But everybody knew that Velo was the sort of guard who never laid a finger on you. The kind of thing he enjoyed was spying through the grille and catching prisoners doing something forbidden, such as playing cards, climbing up to the window, practising gymnastics, quarrelling, using an illegal razor blade, or something similar, so he could send you straight to the punishment cell. Sometimes he liked to play the provocateur. Some said he did this simply to cover up his dodgy deals with the prisoners who worked as cooks and gave him portions of the prisoners' food for his family. Others said that he did such things to anybody who called him Velo instead of Veli, because one of the prisoners had told him that, down in Labëria, Velo is a name given to dogs.

On one of those days when we had lost hope that Çuçi was still alive, Velo arrived and started provoking us. He asked who had pulled out the wire of the cell loudspeaker that hung on the wall. We often did this, so as not to have to listen to Radio Tirana, which made our heads split from morning to night. He wasn't talking to Çavo. But Çavo looked about to explode. He spat back insolently, with a wild stare:

'We don't want to hear your radio. Are you going to force us to listen?'

Velo asked again who had pulled out the wire.

'We're fed up to the back teeth with your lies.'

Velo insisted on asking again who had pulled out the wire.

Then Çavo began to howl in his deep, resonant voice: 'Criminals! Murderers! Soaked in blood up to here, and now you want us to listen to your lies!'

Velo made no reply. Çavo went on shrieking, his eyes bulging. Velo looked scared stiff, and did not close the door, but stood listening. It was very unusual to hear abuse of this kind in Burrel. We knew that anybody who let fly like this would pay a heavy price.

Before he left, Velo muttered something, more to himself than to Çavo. Then he closed the door, shot the bolt, turned the key, and went away. Silence fell on the cell. Everybody was sitting on his pallet except for Çavo, who paced up and down the narrow aisle. We tried to calm him down by looking at him, but he sensed this as soon as he caught anybody's eye, and would start howling in his cavernous voice, fixing on us his furious glare.

'We've put up for long enough with these criminals, the swine!' He listed all the crimes they'd committed, which we had let them get away with, and said that our passivity was the only reason why they had gone so far. If we'd shown a shred of self-respect, even just by killing ourselves and becoming martyrs, they would never have been able to humiliate us in this way.

Finally, Bardhi interrupted him.

'But Çavo, what can we do? They've got the sledge-hammer and we're the nut.'

'We'll be martyrs! We'll be martyrs,' shouted Çavo. 'Our deaths will be on their hands!'

He had acquired some extraordinary spiritual strength, of the kind that overcomes the fear of death. He was ready to sacrifice himself at any moment. He had always been a strong character, and he suffered exceptionally from his humiliation in prison. This made his outburst all the more terrible, and we all understood that the reason behind it was the loss of Çuçi. But nobody mentioned this. He was ashamed to admit that he was ready to die for that little animal, but we all sensed that this was his howl of grief at Çuçi's death.

None of the rest of us were in the state of mind that Çavo asked of us. Qani came closest to it, but he was suffering terribly from stomach pains, and throwing up almost every meal he ate. Pupi had a nervous tic when he clenched his jaw.

There was a great gap between our feelings over Çuçi, and Çavo's. He was a father, whose child had been killed, a lover who had lost his beloved, but we were merely his neighbours. In him, the urge to rebel was strongest, but we were ruled by fear. It was not the cold floorboards of the punishment cell that scared us, but the repercussions of a collective revolt. We couldn't weep for Çuçi, because even though we sorely missed the cat we were ashamed to confess that her loss had so upset us. Not even Çavo could admit it openly. It therefore seemed that he needed to be alone, to mourn his loss in the solitude of the punishment cell, where he would suffer, and suffer terribly, from the iron of the cleats to which they would shackle him, and use this pain to forget the other pain.

After an hour, the door opened and Çavo was summoned.

The next day, the cook who took food to the punishment cells told us that Çavo had been sentenced to ten days chained to the cleats, and yet not a murmur of complaint had passed his lips.

They were forced to strike off his irons on the sixth day, not just because his flesh was cut to the bone but because of infection. The doctor certified that he could no longer be left hanging in chains and he himself wouldn't accept responsibility.

* * *

After a month in the punishment cell, Çavo returned to our room, pale and weak, but also quite calm. Meanwhile, news came that Çuçi's body had been found under the stairs leading to the exercise yard of the opposite wing. They had found buckshot in her body. The story was that after they fired, she had run on, covered in blood, and had leaped through one of the windows of the opposite wing, to reach the corridors of our own, but had collapsed on the stairs. But nobody could prove this to us. It was based on the fact that Çuçi was found inside the prison, where she simply couldn't have been killed.

Another story was she had only been wounded and it was Shukja that had killed her, crushing her in a door as she tried to reach our wing and then throwing her under the stairs.

But we tried our best not to believe either of these versions. We liked to think that Çuçi might still be alive somewhere in the town of Burrel, because she was so beautiful, and maybe one of the guards had taken her home to his family, or to some friend.

John Smith

I

'I've got nothing to do with you filthy Albanians' screamed John, whenever a fellow-prisoner teased him. Then he would hang his head over his wooden knitting needles, from which drooped some unfinished sock or pullover, throw his lame foot forward, and lurch to some other corner in the sun. There he would sit, radiating fury against the Albanians, an aura that took visible form in the clouds of tobacco smoke he blew from his little calabash pipe.

His tormentors watched with expressions of limitless amusement. In fact, they never had any intention of cheating him of his share of the sunlight. They only wanted to goad him into a rage, because repeating this scene had become a ritual of prison life.

John was the only prisoner in Spaç who claimed not to be Albanian; in fact, the entire meaning of his life was invested in his not being Albanian. He firmly maintained that Albanian nationality and citizenship had been forcibly thrust upon him, although he was in fact Australian, and he found himself here because of a disgraceful trick.

Nobody knew his origins in detail, because John, whenever he told his story, would dwell at length on the Australian part, and skim over the Albanian episode in a few words. The question of how this Australian had ended up in Albania remained unanswered. If pressed, he would reluctantly admit that his father was Albanian, but an Albanian of a very low sort, because, according to John, this father had kidnapped him as a small child from his Australian mother and brought him from Australia illegally.

'How? What happened?'

'He put me in a suitcase.'

'What do you mean, in a suitcase?'

'What I said, in a suitcase.'

'And brought you to Albania in a suitcase?'

At this point John's story became obscure. If you persisted, John would tell you that his father was an Albanian who had fled to Australia, where he had an affair with an Australian woman, John's mother. The pair had then separated, and in revenge the father had kidnapped his son, John. So, John claimed, he had been kidnapped as a child from his mother, carried forcibly to Albania, and kept there. Some things still remained unexplained. For instance, how did John know that he had been kidnapped, and not brought here with his parents' consent? Because he had been so small, John replied. What mother would give up her child like that? What state would entrust an infant to its father and not its mother?

Meanwhile, another story was somehow in circulation, no doubt a result of pure speculation, because nobody had any way of knowing what had happened in faraway Australia. According to this version, John's mother had been a whore, and John had been left with his father, because his mother hadn't wanted to keep him. By 'whore', people merely meant a woman who had left John's father for another man. The affair became murkier still if you asked why his father had not been arrested and sentenced for escape when he'd returned to Albania, as happened to all those who returned, but had been allowed to build a normal life?

Because he was a sly peasant, said John, and for the sake of his little son. Prisoners who knew about the fate of returnees supplied a different answer – that his father must have been an agent of Albanian State Security, sent abroad on a mission. But why should the Albanian state be so interested in sending spies to Australia?

It was so improbable that an Albanian villager, at the time of the country's deepest communist isolation, could go to Australia, father a child by an Australian mother, and then return to Albania with this child, that some believed that John had made up the entire story, that there was not a drop of Australian blood in his veins, and that his father had never seen Australia, even in his dreams. Or maybe he had dreamt of Australia and told John about his dream, and John had become convinced that his mother was Australian. Or perhaps John's delusion stemmed from the fact that his mother, his father's first wife, had died very young and left him when he was very small.

Certainly, even the camp authorities recognized his name as John, a very strange name for an Albanian, but officially his surname was not Smith, as he called himself, but Sfrati. He had been sentenced to fifteen years after an attempted escape from a border village near Korça, where he had worked as a driver. John claimed that he was trying to return to his mother in Australia, so this didn't qualify as 'treason to the homeland' under Article 49 of the Criminal Code. He had his own motherland, Australia, and it was his own proper right to seek out his mother. He was an Australian held by force in an Albanian prison, and the problem was that Australia couldn't find any trace of him. There was no Australian embassy or consulate in Albania, and this complicated the matter further, he said.

* * *

Meanwhile, John was a unique character in the Spaç camp for another reason. He was young, indeed handsome, with a fine oval face and an elegant moustache. But he was severely disabled, unable to walk properly on his right foot. He could only walk on the heel, raising the sole into the air. He said that it hurt him terribly to lay the sole flat on the ground. Instead of a prison moccasin, he wore a wooden clog on this foot, attached by a bandage. He admitted that this injury to his foot had been his own fault. A few years before, trying to skive off work in the mine gallery, he had inserted his foot beside a rail as a waggon full of ore had passed, and the wagon's iron wheel had badly damaged the bone at the back of his right foot.

After a lot of treatment, he contracted a particular bone disease that John called by a name that nobody knew. So, in trying to save himself from the mine, he was left lame for life. However, he had succeeded in becoming a permanent member of the unemployed brigade, which most of those who worked the three shifts in the mine gallery considered to be the most blessed position anyone in prison could secure.

John had no help from his family, because his father, who he called 'that cheat' never came to visit him and sent no money or parcels. Yet John never complained of having time on his hands. To supplement the camp ration and to secure the tobacco he smoked in his calabash pipe, which never left his mouth, he would knit the woollen socks and pullovers and caps that prisoners needed. He would also hang around the kitchen, helping in small ways the prisoners who cooked, in return for a portion of food.

He spent the rest of his time composing letters to demand, as he put it, the restoration of his lost Australian citizenship.

But there was another aspect to John that was often apparent in the stories that other people told about him. Those who had known him for a long time in prison said that when he first arrived he'd been different; he came out with his Australian identity only later, and added the anti-Albanian posturing later still. It was said that at one time John had not earned his living as honestly as now, knitting sweaters and socks, but had been a thief, stealing whatever and wherever he could, often in cahoots with the Albanian thieves in the camp.

One story went the rounds involving John and Kosovrasti, the camp's convict doctor. One day, Kosovrasti had cooked a pot of stuffed vegetables in the private kitchen and left it to cool while he returned to his clinic to care for a patient. John, who often visited the private kitchen, noticed the unattended dish. He was hungry. He eyed the pot like a tom-cat and reckoned he could eat the contents without anyone noticing. He started to pace to and fro across the kitchen with a spoon in his hand, and as he passed Kosovrasti's stew he would pick out a stuffed pepper or tomato and gobble it up, until the entire dish was gone. Kosovrasti came back to an empty pot.

Kosovrasti was not given to moaning; on the contrary, he was one of the few prisoners who never showed his feelings, and considered any display of emotion to be a weakness. But he got to work on the quiet to find out who had eaten his lunch. As the camp doctor, he wielded considerable power over the prisoners, and this made his task easier. If John had known that this was Kosovrasti's stew, he would never have eaten it, because, apart from anything else, he had been his regular patient ever since he had stuck his foot under the waggon.

So within a very short time, even before the tomatoes and peppers and rice had settled in John's stomach, Kosovrasti's many spies found out who the tom-cat was that had been prowling round the kitchen. Nobody but John could have eaten the stew.

Kosovrasti approached John tactfully, without arousing his suspicions.

'Why haven't you come to the clinic, John?' he said, 'How's your foot?'

'It hurts all the time,' John replied.

'Come and see me, because some very good medicine has arrived.'

John trusted him. Kosovrasti prepared an injection that induced vomiting, and carefully administered it. John left well-pleased. But he was back before long, complaining that he felt unwell and wanted to vomit. 'It happens with this medicine,' Kosovrasti said, and put a bowl in front of him. And while John emptied the contents of his stomach, Kosovrasti stood over the bowl and counted the peppers and tomatoes and eggplants that John spewed up.

'Those are my peppers. I'd only just filled them, and those are my tomatoes, and the eggplant, and the rice, not even digested yet,' said Kosovrasti in tones almost of sympathy rather than revenge.

Yet John denied the truth of this story, which still went the rounds of the camp, and increasingly so as John insisted more and more on his Australian identity. He called the story a typically Albanian slander. The Albanians were always thinking of food because they'd gone hungry for centuries, whereas he was bred of well-nourished stock and had more elevated things to dream about.

It was impossible to say exactly when John's Australianness became so firmly rooted. There was no decisive moment. But there was a logical progression from John, the hardened thief, to John with his Australian mania, who despised Albania, which had deprived him of his very mother, and everything to do with it. The prison was full of people who craved a virtual escape of one kind or another. Even John's tormentors, who found entertainment in listening to his diatribes against the filthy Albanians, were driven by a deep need to escape the reality of Albania, which had imprisoned them and reduced them to such misery.

But another aspect to John made his personality harder to understand. There were a few prisoners, although not many, who said that everything about him, from his external appearance as a cripple with a wooden clog, to his claim to be Australian, was a total fraud. This mask concealed the sly and vigilant eyes and ears of an inveterate spy, who watched everything and reported anything suspicious to the camp command. These people accused him of using his Australian identity to hide even from himself, because when he was first imprisoned, he'd been a spy among the cells, extracting secrets from men who were then shot because of his reports. These prisoners told stories of how they'd seen him at night, walking perfectly upright to the authorities to deliver his denunciations. These tales had the power to transform the placid, reserved John with his Australian delusions into a frightening creature, one of the most dangerous spies of Spaç.

His most bitter enemy was Çesku, one of the camp's seasoned gamblers, who said that twice he had landed in a punishment cell in winter, caught by the guard playing poker, all because of John, the only person who knew where the game was taking place. Sometimes Çesku said to his face, in front of everybody:

'John Sfrati, self-styled Smith, born of an Albanian father and an Australian whore, brought to Albania in a suitcase, a nasty old spy.'

'I've got nothing to do with you filthy Albanians,' John shouted back, even louder than when he was teased. His Australian identity was so ingrained, it was hard to believe it was a mere front.

But John's strongest defence against these charges was his leg. If he'd been a collaborator of the Security Service or the camp commander, why should he torture himself by walking on the heel of one foot? So many spies lived an easy life in Spaç, thanks to their snooping. It was also hard to find a prisoner against whom there were no suspicions of this kind, because we all lived in fear of the spies in our midst, watching and reporting our every step.

It was thanks to his leg that John was finally rescued from the savagery of Spaç. One day the prison van that brought the new inmates took him away with a number of prisoners of the unemployed brigade, and transferred him to the camp at Ballsh.

II

I too was transferred to the Ballsh camp. When I arrived, among the other prisoners whom I knew from Spaç who came up to greet me, John Smith appeared, extending a welcoming hand. It was the same man, with his calabash pipe in his mouth, his knitting needles, and his patched and unwashed clothes, but he had changed so completely I could scarcely believe my eyes. He walked at a sprightly pace, firmly on both feet. So, for several years on end he had indeed been shamming! How could he have never given himself away, even once? Or had the authorities perhaps known, but left him in peace because of his services to them?

'What is this, John? You really have been a crafty one,' I cheerfully asked him, as did many other people who had known him in Spaç.

John refused to admit that he had been shamming. He said he'd been healed. I reminded him that in Spaç he had described his disease as incurable. He replied that a miracle had occurred. But meanwhile his entire being radiated a challenge which, put into words, would run, 'Do you take me for some piece of Albanian shit like yourself? I'm an Australian, with a will of iron.'

'Any news from Australia, John?'

'I'm doing all I can. I've sent a letter to the Australian Embassy in Belgrade. I'm waiting for a reply.'

Like in Spaç, he continued to knit socks and pullovers to earn something to buy the occasional ration of bread, a kilo of sugar or oil, and loose tobacco.

In Ballsh, he had set himself another task. Here, it wasn't forbidden to study foreign languages, as it was in Spaç. And so he started learning English. He needed it, because one day he would be going to Australia. He boasted of having the proper pronunciation, because it was born into him. Albanians could not pronounce 'ay', 'jay' and all those guttural sounds of English as well he could, but they came to him naturally because of his origins, or because he'd heard them in his mother's womb. This was further proof that he was Australian. From then on, he no longer spelt his name in the Albanian way as 'Xhon,' but John, which was the name, he said, by which he had been registered in Australia, and which had been transliterated under duress into 'Xhon,' as this name was written in the primitive, impoverished Albanian tongue.

In Ballsh, a game also started between him and prisoners who would provoke him into abuse of the people and nation that had brought him up, and now held him so close to their bosom in prison. It was not clear how candidates emerged to play this game, which John himself also no doubt encouraged, because there was no way he could control his rage against the Albanians, and this had now become his way of life in prison.

The game would start with some reciprocal name-calling. When he adopted the name 'John', his tormentors turned it into 'Gjon', the oldest and purest Albanian name for the apostle, used by the Catholics of the north. And when he boasted of his pure English, they would tell him that Australian was something else, nothing but the jargon of transported thieves and criminals.

* * *

Several years passed in this way for John, until one day, after the authorities had distributed the post, he appeared with an envelope in his hand, calling out in joy:

'It's come, it's come! My letter from Australia!'

The other prisoners stared at his face, free for the first time ever from that expression, whether genuine or not, of anger against the Albanians. He laughed like a child. A group of prisoners gathered round him. He showed them two colour photographs, the shape of postcards. One showed a plump woman with large breasts, standing between two young girls.

'My mother and my two sisters,' he said. 'By another husband, not by that cheat.' The other photo showed his Australian brother Paul, a young man of about thirty, also by another father. In the photo, Paul was standing in front of a fence with his dog, which John said was called Dick.

He was keen to show these pictures to anyone who asked. He had found his lost Australian identity, which nobody had believed in. These photographs became his most cherished possessions. But he never read to anybody the accompanying letter. 'It's in English,' he said. 'You won't understand it. Some prisoners said that there was no letter at all, but only the photographs with the names written on the back. Others said that he didn't show the letter because there were things in it that showed that his mother's life hadn't been happy, and she was still miserable and indeed very poor. Another version was that the letter hadn't come directly from Australia, but from his father in Korça, who had been writing to his mother.

'Do they say anything about trying to get you back to Australia, John?'

'Of course they do. Now that they know where I am, Australia won't leave me in the lurch. You're welcome to this crap country you've made for yourselves,' replied John. Yet now he no longer said the 'crap country' with his former rage, but cheerfully, and with a kind of fondness.

There were some who still suspected that this was merely the latest construction of John's Australian mania, or a deception. A man who had practised deception for years, walking on a healthy foot as if he were a cripple, might easily find a couple of photos and claim they were his brother and mother.

* * *

It wasn't easy to sustain cheerfulness in prison, so before long John reverted to his earlier anti-Albanian invective. He had told us to expect food parcels from Australia that would be the amazement of the camp. But no parcels came, nor even a letter, let alone an attempt to secure his release. He blamed everything on the state censor, but went on writing letters to his 'Australian home'.

The prisoners who enjoyed taunting John, and who after the letter had begun to tease him in a more light-hearted fashion in response to his buoyant mood, went back to goading him with the kind of aggression that suited the aura of fury that emanated from him. But John, for his part, had now found one more ally against the 'filthy Albanians': Dick, his brother's dog. New expressions entered John's diatribes: 'Dick eats in one month as much meat as you half-starved buggers have eaten in your whole lives,' 'Dick's foreleg is as thick as your neck.'

No more letters or photographs came from Australia.

Only once, shortly before his release, John's brothers from Korça came to visit him. 'The brothers I have here, from that cheat,' he said to me in a low voice, without prolonging the conversation.

* * *

Down to the very end, he earned his bread from his knitting needles. On the day of his release, he observed the ritual that every prisoner went through before roll-call on the morning of freedom. He wore a suit dating back to his youth, which his brothers from Korça had fetched for him, and was now a little tight. With his calabash pipe in his mouth, freshly shaved, and his moustache shining as never before, he offered round cigarettes from the packets he had bought with the earnings of his wooden knitting needles. Many prisoners gathered round. They hoped that one day his dream would come true and he would go to Australia to see his mother, his sisters, and his Australian brother. The prisoners who had once pestered him also came to share a cigarette. They seemed saddened, because we would all feel John's absence. Who else could answer their need for self-laceration? Who would there be to make such fun of their own tragedy, as did John when he said, 'you filthy Albanians.'

Some of those who congratulated him as they shared a farewell cigarette no doubt also wondered, who was the real John who had lived with them for fifteen years? Was he really an Australian, a crazy Albanian, or a more than usually dangerous spy? Had he deceived everybody with that foot of his, clamped for years to a wooden clog, or had he merely hoodwinked the camp command? Was he right not to entrust his secret to any other prisoner down to the very end, or was this very distrust merely further evidence of his dishonesty? Did he really hate the Albanians, or was this too a game?

He went away, leaving no answers to these questions. But there were few prisoners who walked out of the prison gates on the day of their release without leaving such questions behind. What kind of people had they had really been? Yet, if you think more deeply, what sense is there in looking for an answer?

The Don

He had only ever told his closest friends the great secret of his life: what had happened to him during the month when, shackled by the ankles and wrists and with a helmet on his head, he'd gone through the terror of uncertainty as to whether he would be shot or reprieved? One night, in the small hours as he trembled with the fear that they would come for him, opening the door and handing him over to death in the foothills of Mount Dajti, he had experienced an illumination that had taken hold of his mind and then spread through his entire being and calmed him as if by magic. He heard his wife's voice, saying 'They can't shoot a genius, and you are a genius.'

* * *

Prisoners sentenced to death were held in a cell with hands and feet shackled, and wearing a helmet day and night to avert any possibility of suicide by hanging or hitting their head on some corner of brickwork. A piece of rope three or four metres long was also kept in the cupboard in the corridor by the cell door. This too served to avert any suicide attempts when the prisoner's fetters and handcuffs were removed for his walk to the common latrine to urinate, defecate, wash his private parts, and rinse the bowl and spoon used for his rations.

The handcuffs were also removed when he ate his three meals in the cell and when he was taken for a shower once a week. In these cases, the rope was used as a kind of harness, one end tied round the prisoner's waist, and the other held by one of the two guards on the shift. There had to be a minimum of two guards when any prisoner sentenced to death was moved, and they were obliged to keep him under watch at every moment, even while he squatted above the black hole of the Turkish-style toilet. The guards were to haul him by the rope if he tried to make any suicidal move.

Nobody knew how far these measures had been dictated by the experience of earlier suicides or were part of the sadistic treatment of these creatures who were already reckoned half-dead. The justification was that the convicted man shouldn't be allowed to escape the punishment handed down to him in the name of the people. Prisoners who had been through this situation said that in these conditions before execution you really did almost go mad and become entirely unpredictable, but it was not the rope, the helmet, and the shackles that kept you from suicide, but hope.

Some even said that the physical torture of the shackles, especially the wounds caused by the iron digging into the wrists and ankles, helped alleviate the worse torture, the fear of death. It was this terror, not the pain, that kept them awake in the small hours when prisoners were taken out to be shot. This fear exhausted them until daylight allowed them a few hours of sleep to collect themselves. Then the fear returned even more savagely the next night, which arrived horribly fast.

For a spark of genius to ignite under these conditions, suicide had to be far from your mind. Either your love of life or your fear of death had to be exceptionally strong.

Thanks either to this yearning to live, or to this fear of death, the Don, tied by the hands and feet, had begun to think with increasing intensity and fervour that he couldn't depart this life just like that before reaching thirty, without achieving anything on this earth beyond leaving behind two small children. He said that these thoughts became a nightmarish obsession and generated the obscure idea that he hadn't come into this world as an ordinary mortal, but was chosen for some special purpose.

One blessed night this special purpose became apparent in a light falling on him and his wife's voice telling him that they could not kill him because he was a genius. In the succeeding days the light would fade, and his fear would come back, but slowly and subconsciously he found a way to kindle this light and he would regain serenity, imagining himself becoming a great thinker or writer, penning books that would leave their mark on history. He even outlined the content of some of these books. They involved a penetrating study, deeper than anything before, into the human psyche. This was no accident, because in his situation he had touched the essence of human existence, which would be hard to find in any other circumstances.

From the day he was summoned to be told that his death sentence as a Soviet agent had been commuted to twenty-five years' imprisonment, this light remained a steady glow in his mind.

* * *

After emerging from this indescribable horror and taking his place among the other prisoners in the camp, it didn't occur to the Don to suspect that this light and this voice had been a trick played on him by hope, that inseparable friend to life. His elevated thoughts about what he would achieve through the books he would write in the remainder of his life had not evaporated: on the contrary, his fields of intended future study expanded in his mind as his years in prison passed.

He didn't share these things with everybody, because few would understand. No casting pearls before swine. In the camp at Ballsh, where I first met him fifteen years into his sentence, there was only one person he talked to about his plans. This was another veteran prisoner, Koçi the engineer, with whom the Don shared several other characteristics besides their many years in prison. They were of a similar age, and both had graduated in mechanical engineering. Both had been sentenced as revisionist agents, but Koçi as an agent of the Poles, not the Soviets. Both had endured the calvary of waiting for execution with their hands and feet shackled and a helmet on their head, and the lives of both had been spared.

Yet their friendship would not have prospered without certain differences of character, which balanced them together like two opposite poles. Where the Don was an enthusiast and a dreamer, Koçi had strong and practical common sense, and with his tall, slightly stooped and slow frame, his entire being radiated self-restraint. This contrast led to Koçi giving his friend the nickname 'the Don', which he used when talking to other close friends, but never to the Don's face. Koçi said that the Don's way of denying reality recalled Don Quixote de la Mancha, 'the knight of the gloomy countenance', even though he bore him no physical resemblance. He said of himself, 'I'm like Sancho Panza.'

When Koçi talked about his own state of mind while awaiting execution, he never spoke of the intervention of some ray of hope. On the contrary, he said he had lost hope. He showed unusual frankness in relating how one day they summoned him to the investigator's office and told him that to save his own life he must sign up to collaborate with the *Sigurimi*. He had signed, but after arriving in the camp he'd refused to give any information. After a few years they had handed out another sentence to him, leaving him without hope of ever being released.

Koçi believed that decisions on execution had already been taken as soon as the accusations were made, because most of the charges punishable by shooting were bogus and were fabricated in order to sustain the climate of terror. Yet there were also cases when an order came to reduce the number of executions, and so some prisoners remained suspended between life and death, as had happened to him and the Don. Koçi couldn't say whether the *Sigurimi* had asked for his collaboration before the decision to pardon him or after they had been informed that a reprieve had been issued for him, so they could use him for their own purposes. He said that the *Sigurimi* must have also asked the Don to collaborate while he was waiting to be shot, just as they had asked Koçi himself, but the Don had never spoken about this. The fact that the Don had received the illumination that he was a genius suggested that he hadn't received any promise of reprieve after signing. Perhaps they summoned him later, but the Don, confident that they wouldn't kill a genius, hadn't signed. Or did this illumination come to him on the very day when he had been forced to sign?

* * *

When I met the Don, he was a man of about fifty, short and stout, who walked at a brisk pace with his chest out, incessantly moving his arms forward and back, relaxed and confident. His teeth sparkled and looked extremely strong, with not one missing. When I complimented him on his health, he boasted that he had never been to the dentist and he never caught flu or even colds.

He didn't talk to me about his future plans. He told me not to worry, because our sufferings were coming to an end, and a big amnesty was expected soon. I had recently been given a second sentence, so I thought him crazy and didn't encourage this conversation. Only after I got to know him and became friends with Koçi did I learn about his life and what had happened to him in the cell.

Koçi loved the Don and kept his secrets, but he also needed someone to share with and laugh at the Don's exploits. After a time, I was cast in this role and eventually he and I, together with the Don, became a trio who were often seen together. Sometimes our conversations would go on forever, interrupted only when we were summoned for roll-call or it was time to sleep.

The day came when the Don confided in me too that it was the conviction that they couldn't kill a genius that had kept him alive and strong in the cell. They had done well not to kill him, because when his earth-shattering books appeared they too would be proud of him. The main project that he intended to complete as soon as he was released was a three-volume work on sexuality, Sex I, Sex II, and Sex III. The first volume would be on the male sex, the second on the female, and the third on homosexuality and transsexualism.

But the writing of these books awaited him outside prison. Meanwhile, the main issue was his release. In the camp, his special mind worked continually on working out the day when the great amnesty would come and bring release for us all, and to him the chance to write the books. He had reached the conclusion that we would be home by November. He based his argument on the fact that there had been no amnesty for the last fifteen years, the favourable political situation evident in the softening of the regime, and the complex of international circumstances, not to mention the many items of news that prisoners who met their families brought into the camp.

Those who had known him for some time said that the Don had been arguing this for fifteen years, in all the different camps and prisons where he had been. Every year he collected and wove together, inspired by a passionate desire for freedom, all the hopeful rumours brought by prisoners' visiting relatives into a narrative whereby this year the parliament would declare a great amnesty on the eve of the national holidays of the 28th and 29th of November. He would then preach this prophecy throughout the camp to groups of prisoners, large and small. This made the Don one of the people in the camp with the most influence over the prisoners.

It was not only the prisoners' longing for freedom that brought him this influence, nor the evidence and arguments that he compiled with such tireless passion in these heart-to-heart conversations and in groups. His activities extended beyond words. For two or three months before the day of the expected great amnesty he would also change the way he lived. During this time, he would dress differently, carry himself and behave differently, and eat differently. This period, he said, was a preparation for freedom: we should forget the vices and foul language that we had learned in prison, and relearn the manners of life in freedom. We had to walk and speak better. We had to eat better, insofar as we could, because days of intense activity lay ahead of us, including sexual activity. These changes in his behaviour that were so expressive of his deep convictions, became rites of passage to freedom for some prisoners, and had much greater persuasive power than the Don's arguments alone.

And so the Don became the camp's prophet of the religion of liberation. This faith hibernated in winter, but came into bud and blossomed again in spring and summer, reaching its peak in autumn as the November holidays approached. Without the hope that the Don's faith in liberation inspired, prison life would be reduced to a wintry lethargy, to time that passed without shape or meaning, to merely staring at the plumes of smoke rising from the chimneys of the oil refinery opposite. It was precisely this lack of meaning that made prison intolerable. The Don transformed apathy into an intensive preparation for redemption, which would be crowned with the returning promise of a golden age of freedom.

Like any prophet, he also faced opposition in the camp. Other prisoners were nourished by a different kind of hope, not of an amnesty but the overthrow of the regime, which, they said, was nearing its end with the death of the dictator, whose monstrous crimes had shortened his life. Some of these prisoners accused the Don of encouraging false hopes and even doing the work of the camp commander, who wanted to keep the prisoners quiet and not provoke rebellion.

The most embittered of these prisoners were a group who hated the communists like the Don who had ended up in prison. They always reminded us that the Don had studied in the Soviet Union. These prisoners' prophet was Pëllumb, a young lad who had served only a few years in prison, but never forgot to mention that the communists had shot his uncle immediately after seizing power, and had persecuted his family and left them without an education. He never missed an opportunity to say to some imprisoned former communist: Don't imagine that when your regime falls, we'll all be strolling together down the boulevard, as if nothing has happened. When the time comes, and soon, we'll put you all on trial in just the same way. He would put it bluntly to the Don's followers that they were looking forward merely to a liberation that would free them from a small prison with dignity into a larger prison without dignity. This showed that they had been and remained servants of the regime.

But Pëllumb's supporters were a minority that did not dare to show their beliefs openly, for this could lead either to a punishment cell or even a second sentence. Moreover, at the end of the 1970s no such hope was visible on the horizon. The dictator was only seventy years old and had just announced that he would live to be a hundred, because his family all lived to be ninety and the party would grant him another ten. But even if he died, there were his successors, starting with his Number Two, who enjoyed perfect health. The fall of the regime because of international circumstances or economic collapse was unimaginable.

The division of the world into two camps, with the Albanians and their Yugoslav neighbours on the line of demarcation, appeared stable. Internally, the regime was so strong that even if it fell apart economically, it could send the entire population to canteens, like us prisoners, and give each Albanian a bowl of food, and there wouldn't be a squeak out of them.

Meanwhile most of the prisoners had sentences which they wouldn't complete in their lifetimes. Many of them said ironically that they had ended up in prison because they wanted to live in a system where they could express their thoughts freely, have cars like in the West, and travel abroad to see the world, but now they wanted nothing more than to escape from this hell and to go home to their old bicycle and the warmth of the family hearth. For this they were prepared to keep their mouths shut.

Belief in the Don's religion was much more accessible to this majority, whose ambitions were reduced to the basic human needs that the dictatorship had not eliminated, such as the need for love, a family, something to eat, shelter in your own home, the company of old friends, and the hope of dying among them and being buried by them.

* * *

Koçi and I didn't count ourselves among either Pëllumb's adherents, who believed the regime's days were numbered, or the believers in the Don's great amnesty. Still less did we feel close to Frano or Josif, who wouldn't allow you to use the word 'religion' even metaphorically, for these earthly rumours that were so trivial compared to God's plans for our eternal life. We arrogantly trusted in our own reason which, we claimed, included another dimension beyond that of these blind believers, that is the quality of doubt.

Reason united us with the Don's supporters, who thought that life out in the big prison with our families was better than waiting for a ten-minute visit from them once every few months. And so we told Pëllumb's devotees that it was better if the fall of the regime found us outside prison, because nobody knew how that day would manifest. If it came in a violent form, the regime might liquidate us in prison. Moreover, being on the outside, even before that day came, we might manage a successful escape. But reason, which included the doubts raised by the facts that these believers ignored, would not let us see the light that both these groups discerned at the end of our dark tunnel. It wasn't that we lacked hope of getting out, but we imagined our release at some undefined point beyond the end of this tunnel, and the path towards it remained to be charted by unknown events that only time would reveal. For the moment, we did not detect any signs that augured either an amnesty or the fall of the regime.

For this reason, the Don tried even harder to convince us. Now and again, we caught ourselves listening attentively without interrupting him, while banishing from our minds the facts that undermined his story, as if we too wanted to believe in the miracle he was preaching. But this happened rarely and didn't last long, because facts were stubborn and our conversation would once again become a clash of opposing arguments.

One day, I mentioned in conversation with the Don the theory of a scientist who poured scorn on the rumours of the arrival of UFOs on our planet. I had read his article in the science column of one of the regime's newspapers that was delivered to the prison. The editor's introduction implied that it had been published to mock the Western media, always full of such sensational reports. The scientist said that reported sights of an unidentified object that glittered in the night sky, and then a strange flame, or that somewhere in a forest or some remote area they had discovered traces of the descent of a flying saucer, were mere fairy tales. If UFOs really came, it wouldn't happen more or less secretly. Everybody would see them.

'Our release will also come like a flying saucer, and will land some sunny day, seen by thousands of people gathered below to see it,' I told the Don. 'We won't learn about it from some comment whispered by a guard into a prisoner's ear, or anything like that.'

The Don listened to me carefully and thought for a while.

'That's a nice metaphor,' he said. 'But it has nothing to do with the amnesty I'm talking about. Tell this to Pëllumb and his mates who dream every night of the fall of the regime. I'm talking about something simpler. I say that the regime won't fall, but will gradually soften, and the signs of this softening, that will lead to an amnesty, are visible. It's strange that you and Koçi can't see them.'

* * *

In the autumn of 1980, it became difficult to argue with the Don's many followers. He had persuaded them that the signs of the thawing of the regime were obvious, and there were thousands of them, from the movements and attitude of the guards and officers in the camp to their entirely different behaviour towards the families when they came for visits.

One of the commander's officers had gone so far as to exchange cigarettes with a prisoner. Qatip, one of the most brutal and dour of the guards, had laughed among a group of prisoners when one of them told a joke. But more important than all these signs were various meetings of prisoners with their families who still lived in Tirana. The mother of one young prisoner from Tirana had told her son that she had met a cousin of theirs on the street who had assured her that her son would be home soon, and this cousin was not just anybody but someone acquainted with powerful people who until recently had ignored him in the street, because of his imprisoned cousin.

Reports of this kind would come every visiting day, to be conveyed to the Don, who incorporated them into his narrative and publicised them.

And so came the day when we saw the Don dressed in new light grey terylene trousers with a sharply ironed crease, which he otherwise wore only for visits from his family. These trousers were the most significant sign that the Don was waiting in readiness for the great amnesty. Some of his most committed followers wore the same.

We were very curious to find out how the Don, in spite of all his experiences of disappointment, had succeeded in overlooking the contrary facts that Koçi and I had offered. We told him that this same officer who had traded cigarettes had put a prisoner in a punishment cell only a few days previously, solely because he had been sewing a cap during the reading of the dictator's *Works*. And who was the internal guard who had caught him and reported the misdemeanour? None other than Qatip. But the Don immediately found reasons to discount our objections. Qatip had an ancient antipathy to this person, whom he had caught laughing at him amongst a group of prisoners, and so this punishment didn't affect the general trend. He would repeat even more firmly that never before had an officer traded cigarettes with an enemy of the people. Nor had Qatip ever laughed among a group of prisoners.

It was hard to explain this aberration, when you saw the Don's practical common sense, and how well he calculated how to make the small parcels from his family last the month. It was as if there were two Dons, one the person he'd been until his arrest, and the other, the genius, who had been born in the solitary cell where the first Don had lain bound by the wrists and ankles, awaiting execution. He also appeared to have a mechanism which he engaged, or which engaged itself at critical moments, to switch himself from the ordinary Don into a genius. It was a mechanism that he had discovered or created to dispel the fear of his death sentence. Then the genius Don would come to the fore, leaving to the other, ordinary Don only the simple and commonplace tasks of material existence.

Sometimes Koçi and I asked questions which drove the Don to totally opposite, extreme positions. How was the Don so totally armoured against any feeling of doubt? How did he lack the ability to learn from past failures and mistakes? How was it possible that he was never annoyed in the slightest when we argued against the truths that he preached, in the way that we were irritated by him when he ignored our evidence and arguments? Why did he take no notice even of our warnings that if his predictions didn't come true, his followers would suffer a terrible disappointment? Was he perhaps a calculating fraud, and should we be careful in believing what he said? Were Pëllumb and his mates right when they said that he was merely playing the commander's game, sustaining the prisoners with false hope so that they wouldn't make problems?

No, no, this was impossible, we told each other at once as soon as these suspicions surfaced. He preached with such obvious passion that there was no doubting his own faith in what he said. He resembled more a lover who refuses to doubt his beloved, because his feelings of love are more important to him than the truth.

At other times we wondered if the Don first of all manipulated and lied to himself because he couldn't endure the thought that his life was insignificant, and so took refuge in the fiction that he was a genius who would soon be freed and would display his brilliance to the world. And wasn't his success down to the fact that the majority of prisoners suffered the same sense of frustration, that their life was ebbing away without them becoming the people they really were? And therefore they believed him more easily? But why did we two, who were in the same position, not manage to believe him, but would part from him with the feeling that he had granted us a few humorous moments that flattered our pride in our superior intelligence? Were we in the wrong? Did his spiritual motor have an extra gear of faith, which we lacked, and which made the suffering of prison easier for him and his followers?

He was easy in his mind, because the number of prisoners in the camp who trusted his truth were a majority. This was after all a power game that once more demonstrated that a truth measured by reasoned argument is much weaker than a truth measured by the number of people who believe in it. Wasn't this after all the basis of all religions and power structures – creating an illusion to carry the intolerable weight of reality? And did not the creators of these illusions also become leaders of the community, who in time become unable to tolerate any doubt, because this would put their power at risk?

* * *

The November holidays of 1980 passed without the long-expected amnesty. When the parliamentary session that was to have announced it came to its end, the Don appeared among the prisoners for a few moments only, with a stunned expression and an unsettled gaze that suggested despair.

Then he went to sleep earlier than usual. But the next day he pulled himself together and began talking with his accustomed vigour. He had thought hard overnight and it was clear to him that an unforeseen event must have taken place amongst the leadership, because everything was ready for the big amnesty.

Koçi had warned me that the Don wouldn't admit he'd been wrong. He had also told me something else: that the Don often kindled a small fire from the embers of his burned-out hopes, to warm only himself. He usually kept this flame alight during the winter, until the spring and summer of the following year when he would again stoke the fire of hope for a major amnesty.

And this was what happened again. In the winter of 1980-1981, the Don spent a large part of his free time sitting on his bed in the hut, writing. One day Koçi came to me, eager to share another of these laughable but also worrying surprises thrown up by the Don's obliviousness in his quest for hope.

'Didn't I warn you?' he told me, laughing.

'What?'

The Don had confided to him that he was in the final stages of a thorough study of the Albanian mechanical engineering industry, connecting economic solutions with technical inventions. He just needed a few more days to complete it and send it to the top level, one copy to the Party Central Committee and one copy to the Academy of Sciences. But he wanted Koçi to read it and make some comments and suggestions. He was convinced that this study was the only way to strengthen the Albanian economy after the crisis caused by the break with the Chinese.

A few days later Koçi told me that the Don had given him the manuscript to read. He had leafed through it rather than read it, and after two days told the Don that there were plenty of interesting ideas there.

'I wouldn't say it was nonsense,' he said to me, 'and I advised him to give it to you too.'

I also agreed to take the manuscript, sure I wouldn't tell him it was nonsense. I even read through it more attentively than Koçi. It consisted of three thick handwritten notebooks in a large script, and with formulas on some pages, but filled for the most parts with general ideas on how to transform the engineering industry to produce machinery that would strengthen the national economy. The text did not mention the crisis after the break with the Chinese, but the Don indirectly alluded to it, suggesting that he should be brought out of prison to lead the operation. When I returned the text to him, I made a few comments, more to show that I had read it carefully, and he seemed pleased at this.

At the beginning of March, the Don posted the notebooks and began living with the illusion that on the instructions of the Central Committee they were being studied by experts in the Academy of Sciences and perhaps beyond, in the Ministry of Industry. As soon as these experts had finished their reading, they would come to take him to Tirana for a face-to-face discussion, and then, very soon, on the suggestion of the Academy, would come the order for his release. A genius couldn't be kept in prison. 'And my release,' he told us repeatedly during those days of expectation, 'will be the first sign of everybody's release, because the party will finally understand what human resources were being kept locked up and left unexploited.'

It was at this time that he told Koçi that now, thinking more deeply, he had realised that it was his wife who had discovered the first sparks of his genius, and that in the light that came down to him in his cell the voice that had spoken was his wife's. She had once asked him to pass her the basin to wash their little son, but the Don, lost in his own thoughts, had handed her a cushion instead. His wife had hugged him and said, 'My husband is a genius!'

After this story, Koçi said that the Don had always been like this, and the tale about his cell was either a fiction or a sign of a transition to a more serious narcissistic disturbance.

Round about that time, television arrived in the camp for the first time and a set was placed at one end of the canteen hut, at first on a plank platform one metre high that also served as a stage. The Don also incorporated this novelty into his narrative. It was a sign of a thaw that the prisoners, who for years had seen nothing but their huts, the barbed wire, and the smokestacks of the refinery that they themselves had built, could now also see scenes beyond the wire on the small screen.

But the screen also brought the Don something unexpected. We could see on the black-and-white receiver not only news and documentaries that showed the successes in building socialism in agriculture and industry, but also the occasional film or concert. We could now identify the faces of the singers we heard on the radio. And so one day the Don told Koçi that he had fallen in love with Liljana, a singer with black eyes, curly hair, and full sensual lips, the most beautiful and successful of all the singers of the day. As soon as he was released, he would go to her and make his proposal, for there was no chance that she would fail to fall into the genius's arms. Of course, because of his intellectual powers, he added, not his physical appearance. 'But what about your wife?' Koçi had asked. 'I love my wife. She's the mother of my children. But she can't satisfy me sexually. Liljana will be my secret lover.'

At this point I admitted that Koçi had been right and that the Don's craziness was very similar to that of Don Quixote, the knight of La Mancha. We were missing Dulcinea del Toboso, and now we'd found her too. From that time on Koçi and I would part after our conversations with the Don and say to one another, 'Life is a dream, let me live, don't wake me.'

* * *

When The Don's followers saw him one day at the end of March dressed in terylene trousers, on his walks with his characteristic gait, chest out, and arms swinging in front and behind, they thought he was dressed this way because he was expecting a family visit. But when he wore these clothes the next day and the day after, the Don had to explain that he wasn't sure what day they were coming, and so he had to wear them every day. He couldn't tell everybody the story of the document he had sent to the authorities, not only because his supporters might take this as a betrayal of their collective hopes, but because Pëllumb's group would portray him as a lackey of the regime.

After the failure of the amnesty, this group had been unsparing in accusations of this kind. Some even called him a spy, but it was clear that the Don was nothing of the sort. Spies had a duty to make provocations and talk against the state. But the Don rarely made critical comments, especially about the dictator. In his sermons he even seemed to be trying to present himself as the regime's saviour.

For the first week the Don wore his terylene trousers all day, and then only in the mornings, until one day they became stained. He washed them and spread them out to dry before putting them back in this clothes bag. Then he wore ragged brown camp-issue canvas trousers, but without losing hope that one day he would be summoned. No doubt some jealous character in the Academy must have delayed or misinterpreted his thesis.

* * *

Autumn arrived, but still nobody came from Tirana to fetch him. But the November holidays were approaching and the Don shifted very quickly to a collective hope. He had some of his arguments ready. The earlier amnesty was waiting in a desk drawer and simply had to be approved. This hadn't been done because at the last moment other matters had preoccupied the leadership – to do with the economy, he said to Koçi and me who knew about the famous note-books – but now it seemed that everything was on track.

As if to demonstrate that this time release was inevitable, the Don started on his pre-release rituals with greater determination than ever before. He took it upon himself to re-educate the Limper, the most foul-mouthed prisoner in the camp.

A few months after the fight with Plato and Kujtim, the Limper had been transferred from Spaç to Ballsh, to separate him from his brother Deaf-Boy. But the events at Spaç hadn't changed the Limper. He continued with his filthy language and his unbridled fantasies both heterosexual and homosexual. He could often be seen at the centre of some gleeful group gathered round him to listen to his exploits. His latest fictions were about the exceptional strength of his cock. He boasted of keeping his cock erect for hours on end. What he felt or didn't feel was of no importance, he said, when asked how he kept his satisfaction under control. The point was that no woman or man could resist his cock. Then he related how a well-known woman in his home town had challenged him, and he – what had he done? He had climbed a fig tree and fucked her there for hours on end: cunt, arse, the Limper said, until she gave up. The group round him split their sides.

The Don made his decision one day when the Limper was telling a group that sat round him open-mouthed about how he had fucked a sow. Being a skilled mechanic, the Limper had been employed in the camp's repair show that was situated in the security zone between the two wire fences, where the rooms for visits and the punishment cells also were. There was also a sort of small farm in this space to support the guards and officers, which included a pigsty.

The Limper told how one morning he had woken up with a big stiffy that just would not subside even while he ate breakfast and went out to work. When he went out to feed the pigs, he noticed the commandant's plumpest sow eyeing him provocatively. He went up to her, moved her to one side, and took hold of her until he had penetrated her. The sow had been wonderfully satisfied, before the very eyes of the hogs, paralysed by jealousy.

At this point the Don issued his challenge. How could he allow this person to be released, with this sort of behaviour and language?

'From now on,' he told him, 'You will keep company only with me and we'll have proper conversations. Don't you realise that we have important tasks ahead when we leave? How can you be released with this kind of language, when you have a daughter ready to be married?'

The Limper's friendship with the Don had its origin in the long years in prison they had shared. They both slept in the same hut. The Limper was a believer in the Don's prophecies of release, but he also acknowledged his craziness and could not resist teasing him. He had taken to the Don by praising his weak points: his intelligence and his perfect physique. He exalted his intelligence by telling other people in front of the Don that he himself, an uneducated ignoramus, listened to nobody's advice but the Don's on every subject, and he praised his athletic vigour, telling him to his face that he had the body of the short-statured athletes and footballers who had become the world's finest.

In this way the Limper joined in the Don's game of his re-education. The Limper told him that mentioning his daughter had stopped him in his tracks and he promised the Don that he would stick by him as closely as possible and avoid the prisoners who egged him on to talk about the strength of his cock. Kaloshi, another joker in the camp and a friend of the Don, also joined the game, telling the Don that the Limper was incorrigible and he was willing to bet that the Don would fail in his project to reform him. His bet remained a notional one, because the Don insisted that it would make no sense for Kaloshi to pay off a gambling debt on the day of their release.

And so the Don and the Limper became an inseparable pair. As soon as he came back from his shift at the workshop and had eaten lunch, the Limper would join him for endless walks beside the hut, where everybody knew they had their regular circuit. The two even lined up for roll-call together.

'We always talk about what we'll do when we're released,' the Don told us when Koçi and I asked how the re-education was going, and what methods he used. 'The Limper needs to learn a lot of things, even how to wear a suit because he's never had one, how to put on a tie, and how to eat with a knife and fork.'

Very soon word got around, spread by the Limper him-self, that the Don's student no longer used foul language and no longer talked about the exploits of his permanently erect cock. He had also given up his favourite word *zgërbythje*, or 'dudarse' which he had made up himself, combining 'arse' *bythë*, with part of the sneering word *zgërdhij*, which had entered prison slang to describe any prisoner who was a total dud, entirely useless even for screwing.

Encouraged by the Limper, their friends expressed their surprise to the Don, at how he had been able to reform this man. The Don explained that it was not he himself, but his imminent release that had reformed him. Listening to these compliments, the Limper would sit hanging his head as if in shame, but nodding towards the Don. 'Well, I had a part in it,' the Don would add finally, 'because he takes what I say as gospel.'

Meanwhile the November holidays were approaching, and the Don had even more supporters than the previous year. My theory about UFOs was totally ignored.

Around this time, the Don's wife came for a conjugal visit. He would sleep one night with her. This wasn't a good sign, because according to the Don we would all be home in two or three weeks at the most. But he said that he'd applied for the conjugal visit a long time ago and they had approved it only now, precisely because they knew what was going to happen.

The following morning the Don left the zone where the visiting rooms were and came back to the prisoners' area. Here, laughing as ever, he distributed the post-meeting cigarettes. His followers gathered round him anxiously to hear what news his wife had brought, whether she knew anything about our release. The Limper was there too, and could hardly wait to turn that moment into a joke, asking in front of the entire company how many times he'd screwed his wife that night, because in his top physical condition he must have scored high. The Don replied that news didn't reach the area where his family lived.

He told the truth only to Koçi the next day. His wife had said nothing to him, but it was he who had told his wife that we would be released very soon. 'When I said that, she put her hand under me to reach my arse.' Koçi's eyes opened wide. 'I asked her what she was doing. She said, "I'm looking for your arse because that's where they'll stick your amnesty."' Koçi could hardly contain himself. 'But these people know nothing,' the Don went on. 'I persuaded her and she began to think. "Maybe," she said when we said goodbye. "God willing, you'll come home. We'll be waiting for you."'

Two weeks later the parliament sat, but the word 'amnesty' was never mentioned during the proceedings.

A few days later, the Don suffered another blow. Kaloshi came into the dormitory and announced to the Don in a loud voice that everyone could hear.

'My dear friend! Didn't I tell you that the Limper would never turn into a human being? Didn't I tell you he's the most degenerate creature the world has ever seen? You lost your bet!'

'What's happened?' the Don asked anxiously.

Meanwhile the Limper had entered too.

'What have you done?' the Don asked him sternly.

The Limper hung his head like a naughty child who has been caught out.

'Let me tell you,' Kaloshi said. 'We were in the canteen in the food queue and this man said to the others round about, 'Look guys, see what a cock of steel I have. I bet you that I can shut the canteen door with one hit from my cock. One of the double doors was wide open. He went straight up to it, took out his cock, and slammed the door shut with it.'

The Don's eyes came out on stalks.

'Did you do this?' he asked the Limper.

The Limper, still hanging his head, said in a low voice, 'Yes, I did.'

The entire camp discovered the next day that the Don and the Limper were no longer going for walks together. The Don was punishing him.

'You will keep away from me for two weeks,' he had announced. The Limper got hold of Koçi and others, asking them to intercede and reconcile him with the Don.

* * *

About three weeks after the November holidays, on a cold and windy December evening, the call sign for the eight o'clock news came from the camp's central loudspeakers fixed to a lamppost on the side of the parade ground. There were few people around, because most prisoners were sheltering in the huts.

Usually, the news started and finished with the successes in the construction of our new life under the glorious leadership of the dictator, and the prisoners paid no attention. But now the announcer's voice was unusually earnest, pronouncing the words 'Communiqué of the Central Committee.'

The prisoners who were close to the loudspeaker slackened their pace and pricked up their ears. The communiqué was a bombshell. The Central Committee reported that the second most powerful man in the country, the prime minister, had killed himself after a 'crisis of the nerves'.

The prisoners stopped in their tracks, and looked at the loudspeaker awaiting further explanation, some lengthy obituary accompanied by an expression of grief from the Central Committee. But there was nothing of the sort. The news broadcast continued as usual with the ordinary reports it carried every day. Nor was there any funereal music after the news.

On the next day everybody started to analyse the events. How had it happened and why? What consequences would it have, and was it good for us or not?

'That's why the expected amnesty was never declared,' was the Don's first reaction. There was a conflict between the leader and his second-in-command.

The Don's theory that it was the second-in-command who had obstructed the amnesty was strengthened when, a few months after his suicide, the current interior minister and his predecessor were arrested. Both had been noted for their savagery.

Meanwhile there was nothing on the radio and television news about the motives behind the suicide and the charges against these others. The meetings of the Politburo where these persons' first trials took place were held in secret. Obviously, they were enemies, but the dictator would say in due course what kind of enemies. He made only one appearance a short time after the prime minister's suicide, in the Art Gallery among the artists and writers closest to the party. He talked to them about the care shown by the party for literature and art, but let fall a half-finished phrase that suggested that he had chosen them to talk to about the unexpected event that was in all of their minds. 'But... you know... and we know...' The artists and writers of his court pricked up their ears for what he would say, but he left unfinished whatever he had in mind.

It seemed that he had let slip that phrase involuntarily, under the pressure of his thoughts, but then realised that he had turned up to demonstrate that on the contrary, his mind was easy, and also perhaps that he was fit and well, and not as his enemies might be hoping.

The Don soon devised his own version: the leader-in-chief would denounce the regime's number two, the interior minister and their accomplices as sectarians, and the main culprits for the mass arrests of the 1970s. The Don did not have the slightest doubt that the leader was attempting thereby to erase his own mistakes. He did not say this to everybody out loud, but he implied it. He said that reliable reports had reached the camp that the former interior minister had been accused at a Politburo meeting of attempting to estrange the party and the leader-in-chief from the people, and to this end had arrested innocent people merely for expressing discontent that there wasn't enough meat, milk or cheese in the shops. The minister and his henchmen were also responsible for the second sentences dealt out to prisoners before they had finished their first, thus creating a poor image of justice in our country.

'Your theory about UFOs has collapsed,' he said to me one day. 'This time the flying saucers are coming down in full view of everybody. Look, a fearful prime minister who was previously interior minister, and the two latest interior ministers, each more savage than the last – what other charges can they face besides state terrorism?'

* * *

The entire year of 1982 was taken up with discussions of these events and awaiting the consequences.

Meanwhile the dictator had still not expressed his view and had not even appeared in public since his visit to the Art Gallery. Some people said there had been an attempt to poison him, and he was very ill.

When November came almost the whole camp was prepared for an amnesty. No date was announced for the parliamentary sitting. But the news spread that the dictator would announce the release of prisoners in a speech he would make himself.

The Don was also fantasising about where he would go on holiday and how he would introduce himself to Liljana. Koçi and I didn't dare voice our arguments that cast doubt on the great amnesty. Indeed, deep down we too had been swayed. Who knows, we said to ourselves, anything might happen, although it seemed to us impossible that the dictator would admit that his convicted enemies had been innocent. But the Don said that this had happened before, in 1947–1948, when the dictator had broken with Tito and blamed the then interior minister for an excess of imprisonments and sentences, accusing him of being a Yugoslav agent.

* * *

On the eve of the November holidays the dictator indeed made a speech of the kind that the propaganda called 'decisive'. All the prisoners gathered in front of the television in the canteen and listened with bated breath.

The dictator looked sterner and more concentrated than usual, which disappointed those who hoped he was ill. He began his speech as always by listing the great successes that had been achieved thanks to the party and its leadership and its correct line, 'which no enemy has been able to bend,' he emphasised in a loud voice. This was a familiar phrase, but this time it came as a cold shower. If the line hadn't been bent, then our imprisonment was justified. In fact, how could anyone dare to think that the dictator would expose himself as negligent, by admitting publicly that people who had always been his subordinates had bent the line? That had indeed happened in 1947, when he had just taken power, but it wouldn't be allowed now after three decades in which he had worked to create his cult of the absolute leader. So what was going on?

Now even the most optimistic began to have their doubts, as the dictator took up the theme of his most recent enemies.

'They couldn't bend the party line in the slightest,' he repeated. 'They could only camouflage themselves a little longer than the others, but the party exposed them.' Then he dropped his bombshell: the second-in-command and his recent accomplices had been the leaders of all the hostile groups that had been discovered in the past. They had gone so far as to plan to assassinate the leader himself.

'Let them pay for it!' shouted a voice from the hall.

'That's right!' the dictator replied.

The entire hall rose to its feet and burst into long applause, chanting the dictator's name endlessly.

This was the worst moment for us. Despair settled on the entire canteen. The wreaths of tobacco smoke above the prisoners' heads turned into a black cloud. Even the Don, who never smoked, had lit up.

But soon everything changed. At the end of his speech the dictator, reverting to the successes of socialist construction, paused and added... 'These successes are also proved by the extensive pardon that the Presidium of the People's Assembly has decreed, which will be published tomorrow in *Zëri i Popullit*.

This time it was the prisoners who burst into applause. But not all of them, for there were also sceptics and those who were ashamed to applaud.

So there was no need to summon the parliament. They had chosen a pardon that was within the competence of the Presidium. But could a pardon be the equal of an amnesty? After hearing the speech, Koçi and I could not come to a conclusion. The Don was in seventh heaven. No prisoner would be excluded from the pardon.

Nobody slept that night, waiting for the morning's newspaper.

* * *

The newspaper *Zëri i Popullit* came early every morning, but on that long-expected day they didn't bring it into the camp. Around noon they ordered all the prisoners to assemble on the parade ground. At last, one of the guard officers arrived, holding a copy of the newspaper. Evidently he would read out the decree.

The text was short, over in the blink of an eye, and cast almost everybody into a pit of disappointment. Only two categories of prisoner were pardoned: of those sentenced for agitation and propaganda, only those aged over sixty and those sentenced to less than eight years were freed, and also those with less than one year of their sentences left. The remainder were pardoned one quarter of their remaining sentences. Those sentenced for such offences as espionage, membership of counterrevolutionary organisations, terrorism, and sabotage were not pardoned a single day, and nor were those with second sentences. So both Koçi and I, and the Don as well, remained exactly where we were.

The guard officer went away, leaving behind a despondent atmosphere. The fortunate, who ironically were those who had served the shortest time in prison, couldn't celebrate because of the majority who were being left inside. Of the prisoners excluded, even those who had never nourished any hopes felt let down. Pëllumb and his fanatical followers confined themselves to ridiculing this mockery of a pardon, and merely used Pëllumb's favourite expression about 'hunchbacks straighten up only in the grave.' That day Koçi confided to me the great regret of his life; something that he had never confessed before:

'If only I had a child, I wouldn't mind spending my whole life in prison. I would like just to have a child.'

But the Don did not give in. He called this merely the first phase of the great amnesty.

* * *

The prisoners freed under the pardon went home, wishing the rest of us a speedy release. The emotional vacancy left by their departure was quickly filled with a report that alarmed us all. We had to gather our belongings, because we were going to be transferred. The pardon had required a reorganisation of all the camps and prisons. Where would they take us? What lay ahead?

When the transfers began, we realised that we would not all be sent to the same camp. One group, mostly the over-sixties sentenced for crimes that were not amnestied, ended up in a camp for elderly prisoners near the town of Lezhë. Koçi and the Don left with another small group of prisoners over forty. It was rumoured they were going to Spaç. When we said goodbye, I said I hoped to see them again in some camp, but the Don insisted that we would meet very soon in freedom. I embraced him and said, 'I hope so!'

Along with the group of younger prisoners, after an eight-hour journey in a covered truck I ended up in the camp of Qafë Bari, where there was a mine in which ordinary criminals had worked. It was a terrible place, colder and more isolated even than Spaç, and it was clear from the reception we got from the police personnel that the treatment would be harsher than at Spaç. Besides the climate, there was the hard labour in three shifts in the mine. But after three months, the unemployed brigade, of which I was part, was taken out of there and sent to Spaç. There among other familiar fellow-prisoners I found the Don and Koçi.

It was not long before we found out that the remaining political prisoners in Spaç wouldn't work in the mine because only a small number were capable of mine work, and most of them had been sent to Qafë Bari. News came that ordinary criminals would be brought in to work in the mine. They would be accommodated in the main block, where we had been put for the moment, and we would be moved to the huts in the annexe beyond the stream. This was a small camp in itself, inside the main wire, and it was connected to the main building by an iron bridge covered with barbed wire, whose piers rested on the two banks of the stream. About a hundred selected ordinary criminals with short sentences had served their time there, given jobs that couldn't be entrusted to politicals, such as maintaining the wire or uprooting all the vegetation close to it that might otherwise offer cover for an escape attempt. We were one hundred metres from them as the crow flies, but much further in terms of our treatment because whenever the authorities visited and met with them, they were told that in the event of war they would be given weapons to fight for the homeland, whereas we would be shot.

Under the pardon, almost all of them had been released, for their sentences had been short, and their huts appeared empty. One day they ordered us all to assemble in the yard with our belongings. They subjected us to a detailed search and escorted us over the iron bridge to the little annexe.

A few days later we could see from there that the main block was filling with a very large number of ordinary criminals.

* * *

The work brigades of ordinary criminals which from then on began to climb the path on the opposite bank of the stream passed us at the closest point no more than thirty or forty metres away. Most of these prisoners were lads in their twenties. Three times a day, according to the same timetable of shifts that we had worked, these unfortunate creatures climbed up and down the bare reddish-coloured mountain whose bowels contained the glittering store of copper pyrites. But we noticed quite soon that the line of the ordinary criminals' work brigade was more ragged and ill-disciplined than ours had been.

Every day we witnessed terrible scenes of the beating of ordinary criminals who refused to climb the mountain to work. The skies rang with their shouts and screams. The punishment cells were crammed with ordinary criminals who refused to work, but now and then one of us was also sent to the cells. They brought back harrowing stories of the methods these boys resorted to in order to avoid work. Some of them, to render themselves incapable, blew off two fingers with dynamite, disabling themselves for life. Others swallowed lengths of wire or injected shit or oil into their bodies so that they could be sent to hospital, where they opened their stomachs to remove the wire or cure the infections. Others climbed on to the ridge of the dormitory roof and threatened to jump.

These scenes and reports made us consider whether we had been more resigned to our fate or more resistant to the suffering of mine work. Or perhaps we valued life more than these boys. Whatever the reason, our status and behaviour won more respect from the brutal guards of Spaç, even though their chiefs had told them that in war the ordinary criminals would be given guns, and we would be shot.

* * *

The Don had never been in Spaç before. He had heard that the sort of treatment we witnessed also occurred with the politicals, but what he saw struck him as repugnant, especially now. He was still convinced that the party line had begun to change with the sentencing of the two terrifying former ministers. He told us that the treatment we saw could only represent the vestiges of their rule. Koçi told me that the Don had set in motion his mechanism to create new, personal hope for himself.

One day we heard the story of an ordinary criminal who had not gone out to work. When they had come after him to catch him and beat him, he had run to the toilet, smeared himself from head to foot in shit so that the guards wouldn't come near him, and climbed onto the roof terrace of one of the blocks.

'I can't let that pass,' the Don said. 'Let me tell you I'm writing to the Central Committee to describe the inhuman treatment of the ordinary criminals here. I'm telling them that the Directorate of Camps and Prisons has been turned into a *refugium peccatorum* for all the incompetent and ignorant officers of the Interior Ministry. Prisons should be places of genuine re-education and work cannot be made compulsory by force in a socialist country. But here prisoners are reduced either to going out to work in the mine or choosing between being beaten to death by the guards and dying in a punishment cell. I also describe the acts of self-mutilation they're forced to commit, and this most recent case of the man who smeared himself in shit to avoid being beaten. I'm asking the Central Committee to take immediate measures to improve this situation.'

When we learned he'd sent the letter, we were worried. Replies in such cases were swift. How would they reply to a letter prompted by such a huge misunderstanding on the part of our Don Quixote, who had taken it on himself to be the saviour of both God and his devils?

* * *

The Don received his reply when the time came for the regular inspection. Once a month, the police entered unannounced into the camp, and after body searching us one by one, gathered us in a corner of the yard and made a detailed search of the dormitories, the storehouses, and everything else on the territory of the camp.

After completing the search, they summoned the Don and escorted him to his bed. A policeman held in his hand a long nail, which the Don supposedly had hidden under the bed, as a weapon.

The Don told them the nail was nothing to do with him.

The policemen took him to the guard officer, who ordered them to take him into the forbidden zone where the punishment cells were.

One month in the punishment cell was the minimum, and Koçi and I wondered what else they had in store for him. Obviously, the letter was the reason.

We were surprised when he returned only a few hours later, with a very pale face. We went up to him at once.

'What happened?' we asked.

He signalled to us that we should step aside quietly. We went to a corner of the hut. Meanwhile dusk had fallen.

The Don lifted his shirt and showed us his back and belly, totally black with bruises, apparently from countless truncheon blows.

'What are all these?'

He told us in a soft voice that when he entered the zone, all the officers of the camp command gathered round him. First the guard officer asked him about the nail. The Don made no bones about telling them that the nail wasn't his, but they had planted it themselves in revenge for the letter he'd sent to the Central Committee. This drove them wild. They stretched him out on a plank and tied him to it. They all beat him with truncheons in turn. When half the officers had worn themselves out on his back, they turned him over and the others started on his belly. 'Did you want to put us out of work, you son of a bitch? We're not up to our jobs? Now see how incompetent we are,' and they beat him with all the strength they could muster.

We were left speechless. We couldn't even say it had been a mistake of his to send the letter, because he was quick to give his own reasons.

'I thought they'd put me in solitary, but they didn't want to leave a record of the punishment. I'm sure that people from the Central Committee will come to meet me, and these guards were scared that they would find me in a cell.'

The next day his wounds hurt less. The Don began to wait with his usual confidence, but still he said to us,

'Anyway, I did my duty to my fellow-prisoners, because those boys are prisoners just like us.'

A few weeks later they came for the Don and transferred him to a different camp.

When he left, Koçi and I missed him more than we had ever imagined. Our camp was a much gloomier place without him. We felt this particularly when the November holidays approached, and we imagined the Don among the prisoners in his new camp, convincing them that the great amnesty was due.

Edip

It was hard to imagine anyone pointing to Edip if they were asked who the famous officer was, sentenced by the dictator with the group of putschists. With his high brow and thick-lensed spectacles, he stood out among the prisoners whose shorn heads and prison clothes made them all look so similar. He resembled more a professor who had spent his entire life in libraries, certainly not in the army. His exceptional courtesy was far from anyone's idea of a military man. He spoke with a soft, measured voice, and chose his words carefully. He was never heard to quarrel or trade insults with anyone in that camp where arguments and squabbles were the order of the day.

* * *

The contrast between his reputation and his appearance prompted a lot of speculation about what lay hidden behind those spectacles with their thick lenses in round frames. The first, unavoidable question was how the dictator could have included this gentle and placid man on the list of putschists and sentenced him to twenty-five years.

The prisoners had different answers. Most believed that Edip's courtesy was the result of a transformation that took place after his investigation and trial. It was hard not to emerge unchanged after being held in a cell for two years, in a lidless coffin with a light bulb glaring twenty-four hours a day above your head – this, they said, was how the putsch-ists were treated – and with the fear of death in your guts; and this, people added, was after a trial which handed out swathes of death sentences. No, he was inevitably a trau-matised man whom his own family would barely recognise, they said, thanking their stars that their own charge sheets and investigations had not been so terrible.

But besides this majority, there were also two groups split into extreme camps. One was composed of former communists who had ended up in prison, who knew Edip better. No, Edip had always been courteous. Why had others who had experienced similar fates not turned to polite-ness? they asked, arguing against the trauma diagnosis. The nobility that he radiated arose from the fact that he was brought up in the family of a high Ottoman aristocrat who had adopted and raised him as a little boy. He had acquired all the virtues of this class to which he had belonged in his youth, but his sensitivity towards the poor had led him to adopt communist ideals and join the antifascist resistance. For his feats in what they proudly termed 'the Struggle' or the 'National Liberation' and his good education, he had been sent immediately after the war for further study in the Soviet Union, at the Air Force Academy. His academic prowess and his exemplary service had lifted him through the ranks until he become Air Force Commander. But the dictator as he aged became increasingly scared of those former comrades of his who had earned their positions through their own merits and not his patronage.

At the other extreme was Pëllumb's anti-communist group, who saw Edip as a victim of persecution. 'The communists are criminals,' Pëllumb insisted. 'They boast of having seized power through bloodshed, and they will only surrender it with bloodshed. Edip hadn't ended up in prison because he had repented of the crimes he had committed against his own class, but because of in-fighting. If their power were ever put in danger, they would all of them, including even those in prison, unite against us, because they are bound together by their crimes.' Pëllumb considered Edip's courtesy to be hypocrisy, a mask that he used to keep his distance from his fellow-inmates, especially the anti-communists like Pëllumb, whom he was afraid to cross.

Against the background of all this opinion and speculation the former Air Force Commander continued to behave with his extraordinary manners towards everybody, leaving open the question of whether this was his true character, a change in his personality caused by his arrest and sentence, or a self-protective mask.

* * *

One prisoner took a different view of Edip's history to everyone else. This was Spiro, a so-called veteran because of the many years that he had behind him. In more than fifteen years his entire being had adapted to the prison environment. His frame was slender, as if to withstand hunger, and his pointed moustaches were yellow from the roll-ups that he smoked continually. His carefully patched clothes, faded of all colour by the sun, and the cap he had sewn himself made Spiro a character that you couldn't imagine with a life outside prison. He was the son of an old communist whom the dictator had eliminated at the start of his time in power. When he grew up, Spiro had tried to escape the country, but he was caught and sentenced to twenty-five years.

Because his own story was linked to the dictator's purges within the party, Spiro knew more than anyone about all the hostile anti-party groups. He could state exactly the dates and names of those purged, the pretexts that the dictator had used, and especially his true, deeper motives which were kept secret. Spiro boasted of possessing these secrets and he had the further skill, which the majority did not have, of discerning the connections between the various purges from the end of the war down to the present.

Spiro explained Edip's courtesy in an entirely different way to Pëllumb. He agreed that it was a mask, but was nothing to do with hypocrisy or fear of the anti-communists or any sense of guilt towards them. The truth was that he was one of the most important figures in the Ballsh camp sentenced by the dictator in his three decades in power. He was the most senior among all the servicemen who were gathered in Hut No. 3, and therefore he had to wear a mask to protect himself, for he was under constant surveillance.

* * *

Hut No. 3, where Edip slept, was different from the others, and was kept cleaner and painted more often with fresh limewash. Someone had even planted a trailing plant by its door, called a 'clock flower' because its flowers resembled the face of a pocket watch.

Most of the convicted communists ascribed this special attention to the aura of power that the inhabitants of this hut still radiated in prison. Almost half had been ministers, deputy ministers, members of the Central Commission, senior military men, parliamentary deputies, or diplomats. Some had been expelled from the party as Tito-ite deviationists in the first years after the war. Others were purged as Khrushchevite revisionists and anti-Stalinists in the '60s. The majority had been arrested in the '70s as ideological liberals, economic saboteurs, and senior servicemen in the Defence Ministry. These were known as the putschists.

According to Pëllumb, the special care of Hut No. 3 was a privilege extended to those who had been enemies from the very start. When the 'clock flowers' at the door bloomed he ridiculed these filthy communists and said the time would come when they would pay for their crimes.

Spiro again deviated from these versions with his own interpretation of the upkeep of Hut No. 3. He linked it to his explanation of Edip's mask. This hut was limewashed more often because there was always work going on in the walls, which were full of surveillance devices. There was a reason why some of the most seasoned provocateurs among the camp spies slept there. The dictator's enemies, who had once been within the Party, had to be watched because some of their accomplices might still be at large, continuing their activities.

Indeed, investigators continually came from the capital, summoning inmates of Hut No. 3 for questioning over their possible connections to people who had been arrested as their cronies. Edip had been summoned several times, and so he was careful even inside the camp. Even to mention in passing the name of some friend of yours outside, if this were picked up by the wrong ears, could cause grief both for him and yourself.

But Spiro went further in his theory of how Edip's mask had become second nature. He was in another kind of danger and was scared. He was wary of revealing the true reasons why the dictator had decided to purge the armed services, which in turn led to the real, deeper truth that had to be kept hidden: the dictator's mental illness. It was this secret, Spiro said, that connected all the purges that he had carried out.

When it came to the army putsch, Spiro scoffed at the simpletons who lamented its failure, because its success would supposedly have freed us from prison. He said that this putsch had been an invention of the dictator from the very beginning. When the first convicted servicemen arrived in the camp, he was not in the least curious to know who had betrayed them, but only what intrigues were afoot in the court of the dictator, whose psyche was now so disturbed that he was imprisoning his most loyal adherents.

Spiro liked to quote a passage of Shakespeare, when the unfortunate King Lear says to his daughter 'Come, let's away to prison... and talk of court news'. Spiro said that prisoners have their antennae tuned to the court. They yearn to be free, and they know that if the day of their release ever comes, it will happen because of events at court. He kept in with every serviceman who arrived in the camp, asking questions intended to ferret out what was happening there.

After his first researches, Spiro began claiming success in shedding light on the mystery surrounding this unexpected blow against the Army. He would confide his interpretation to people he trusted, without mentioning his sources. He would present a complete story without even allowing you to interrupt, still less ask, 'Who told you this?'

* * *

According to Spiro, the story of the imprisonment of Edip and his friends was linked to the dictator's heart attack. One cold day in December 1973, the dictator had returned home after a long meeting, at which he had lit and stubbed out innumerable cigarettes, and felt a strong pain in his chest. Spiro would add as an aside that the dictator was a chain smoker, because of his crimes, and an enfeebled diabetic. The heart attack left him unconscious, hovering between life and death, and for several days he was not moved from his villa. They had brought all the required equipment to the first-floor salon adjacent to the bedroom where he lay.

The members of the Politburo came and went in the drawing room downstairs, alternating in shifts. They spoke to each other in low voices, but would fall silent and listen attentively when the dictator's wife came down from the first floor to tell them the doctors' news.

The fate of Edip and his superiors was decided in that drawing room. One morning, the dictator's wife noticed the defence minister engaged in a very serious conversation with the regime's number three. She sneaked up without being noticed and pricked up her ears, thinking they were maybe talking about her husband's condition, and might have some extra information that the doctors hadn't revealed to her. The defence minister was telling number three that if number two took power they were all in danger, and so they had to take steps as soon as possible.

The dictator's wife panicked. It seemed to her that the wives of some of the Politburo were no longer showing her their usual respect. When the dictator recovered, she was quick to tell him about the shock she had experienced in those grim days, and especially what she'd heard from the mouth of the defence minister himself in the drawing room downstairs.

* * *

Spiro knew French and when he talked about the moment when the dictator's paranoia was unleashed, he would use the French word *déclencher*. This was the key word in his research into the dictator's mania that was a consequence of his crimes. Spiro said that there was no equivalent in Albanian, and the word 'provoke' was closest, but this lacked the same immediacy, the sudden trigger effect of the French word.

His wife's account of the conversation between the minister and the number three, according to Spiro, had *déclenché* the paranoia that was ready to erupt inside him, aggravated already by his terror of death after the heart attack. The dictator had once again proved the truth of what his paranoia told him; that even those who were supposedly his greatest admirers could barely wait for him to die so they could take his place. He decided that the defence minister and many others would go to the grave before him.

Before long the dictator told the state's number two that he had facts to show that the ministers and his accomplices were plotting something. This was enough to launch an investigation. The dictator knew that the minister and his colleagues were working on new policies for the country's defence in the event of an American or Soviet military attack. This is where the investigation should start, he said to himself. He telephoned a senior army leader who had been a partisan in the brigade he himself had led during the war, and invited him to his office. He asked him all sorts of questions, without suggesting that he suspected anything. Then, at a certain moment, when the officer was explaining the strategy under which the army, considering the enemy's strength, would withdraw to the mountains and switch to guerrilla warfare, the dictator found his pretext.

'We waged guerrilla warfare when we were weak during the Liberation War, but now we must face up to the enemy on the battlefront,' the dictator told him the next day. How can we surrender the cities to the enemy? This plan smacks of defeatism, if not treason.'

The defence minister, when he received the order to stop work on the new strategy and send in all the materials for review, took fright. He asked for a meeting with the dictator, and reminded him that they had discussed the new strategy together. But the dictator gave him a cool reception. His mind seemed elsewhere. Perhaps he was listening to his own paranoia, which told him that this traitor would take him up to the mountains and get rid of him there before going back down to seize power with the enemy.

And so the defence strategy was declared 'fatal' and the minister and his comrades were summoned to a plenum and declared traitors. When they left, they were taken straight to cells where they were put in open coffins with light bulbs glaring above their heads night and day, accused of planning to kill the dictator and overthrow the power of the people.

* * *

When I managed to introduce myself to Edip and talk with him, I noticed that his academic appearance was not entirely unrelated to his military career. He dressed neatly, and was always buttoned up, as I imagined academics dressed. And despite the bags under his eyes, enlarged by the thick lenses of his spectacles, his drooping cheeks, and his stomach sagging with age, you could tell that his body possessed a soldier's inner physical strength, imperceptible from a distance. I was especially struck by the soft and measured tones of his voice. In conversation, he asked questions more than he talked himself: how many years was my sentence? Which of my relatives kept track of me in prison and what had happened to them after I was convicted – ordinary topics of conversation between prisoners when they first met.

After this meeting, we started to walk together now and again round the parade ground, until one day I told him about Spiro's version of the reason for their arrest.

He smiled and fell silent a moment, making me think I shouldn't have broached this subject, but then he said to me:

'The only truth in this story is that the defence minister wasn't on good terms with number two and for this reason was discharged from the operation purging the army. As for the rest, it was all untrue. The minister would never have dared to talk to number three against number two in that way. The members of the Politburo don't trust one another as people imagine, thinking that they fought together in the war. Most of them have risen to where they are because of direct connections with the dictator, without being friends with one another. He is the one who holds them together. And then our minister was one of the most trusted people of "number one", as he called the dictator, and could never have conceived of the dictator's death.'

* * *

When I met Spiro, I told him that it was perhaps only the last part of his account that held water.

'I know,' he said.' Other people have also told me that. But the paranoia is true. It remains to be seen why it was *déclenché*.

155

A few days later, I noticed that Spiro was meeting the prisoners of Hut No. 3 increasingly often. I also saw him walking round the parade ground with Edip. I could imagine what they were talking about. Would Edip open up to him, I wondered. Spiro had shown he was a man of his word, with many stints in punishment cells. He also had a distinct ability to make people confide in him.

Before long Spiro began telling his trusted circle a new version of what had *déclenché* the dictator's paranoia against the military.

He also related the story to to me, in his characteristically confidential manner, as if it were told by a third person, without allowing me to interrupt to ask who was the source. But I imagined throughout that Edip was behind this history.

Spiro said that he stood by his first version, but added that the dictator's paranoia had been *déclenché* for a second time, which led to the deadly blow to the minister and his closest associates.

The second *déclenchement* happened after the military delegation's visit to China. This visit took place shortly after his heart attack. It was the period of ping-pong diplomacy between China and the United States, a step on the part of the Chinese that wasn't at all welcomed by the dictator. He straightway sent the Chinese a long letter in which he described this policy as surrender to American imperialism, the revolution's greatest enemy. It wasn't clear what had driven him to send this letter, given that the country's economy was kept afloat with Chinese aid. Spiro claimed that it was a delusion of grandeur combined with a paranoid fear that he might suffer at the hands of the Chinese the fate that he had avoided after Stalin's death, when the Khrushchevite revisionists had wanted to remove him from power as a Stalinist.

The Chinese didn't reply to the dictator's letter, and left the Albanian trade minister, who had gone to China to ask for grain, hanging around Beijing for two months without granting him the meeting he'd requested with the Chinese prime minister.

This silence continued until one day Zhou Enlai said he was ready to receive an Albanian military delegation which had been insistently demanding to visit China because the army had serious shortages of spare parts.

* * *

The senior members of the military delegation, who had already been to China on previous visits, noticed in the reception room of the embassy in Beijing that the photo of the dictator wearing a cap like Mao had been replaced with one of him wearing a fedora. They also found there a furious trade minister, who had been obliged to traipse round all the museums of Beijing with a totally insignificant guide. The trade minister was pleased that the military delegation had finally come, because this meant that he too was invited to a meeting with the Chinese premier. He was impatient to finish his job and go back home.

The ambassador had warned them that after the dictator's letter the signs of a chill were clear, and nobody knew what Zhou Enlai might say to them the next day.

Tea was served and Zhou told them that he was aware of the Albanian Army's needs. The delegation tried to go into details, but Zhou quickly pointed the conversation in a new and unexpected direction. He turned to the trade minister and apologised for the delay in meeting him, but he hadn't summoned him because after two years of difficult harvests China didn't have enough grain for itself.

The delegation remembered Khrushchev saying that the mice in the barns of Ukraine ate as much grain as little Albania needed. But they said nothing, waiting to hear where Zhou was leading.

We had to buy grain from the capitalist world, he continued, and at last grain is arriving from Canada and Australia. But you are against us having any dealings with the capitalists. Isn't that right?

Zhou was clearly alluding to the dictator's letter and implying that the Albanians were behaving like a mangy dog with its tail still held high. Everyone looked at the defence minister. He was the most important member of the delegation, as well as the only Politburo member, and was responsible for speaking first. But the minister was thinking of the dictator's instruction to him before they left. 'Don't on any account come back empty-handed, and avoid any provocation.' He would have liked so much to call Tirana at that moment, and get personal approval for the silence he was maintaining, but Zhou Enlai had closed the meeting with the promise that China would to its utmost to meet their country's need for grain and weapons. The silence of the military delegation had fateful consequences.

On his return from Beijing, the minister hastened to report to the dictator that the visit had ended successfully. The dictator refused to see him in his office, and the minister was astonished to see additional civilian guards at the entrance. The dictator, after being told what had happened in the office of the Chinese prime minister, was at first furious that the military men hadn't spoken up in support of his letter. Then he was overtaken by paranoia: this silence, he thought, was not the result of caution, in order not to jeopardise the arrival of grain and military aid. Beijing had in fact hatched a conspiracy against him, and the minister and his comrades, who fifteen years earlier had stood by him against the Soviets, had now betrayed him to the Chinese.

The remainder of his story was the same as the first version: the dictator had gone to number two and said that they should no longer trust the army chiefs.

There was no doubt that parts of this story had come from Edip's mouth, because he was the only member of the delegation now in the camp. But had he told it to Spiro? Exactly as Spiro related the story, certainly not. Edip could never have talked about the paranoia of 'number one'. This was Spiro's interpretation, incorporating what Edip had told him into his own account of the dictator's paranoia.

* * *

After number two's suicide, I met Edip more often.

Previously, when talking about the conviction of himself and his military colleagues, he would comment on it in a spirit of resignation to fate. He nurtured a vague hope that he wouldn't spend his entire life in prison, but went no further than that. Now I noticed that he was prepared to talk more. I also noticed that he knew more than I thought about the rumours that went round the camp, and the camp's well-known personalities. He knew that the Don had rekindled the prospect of a major amnesty on the grounds that the dictator would ascribe all his crimes and extremism to the former prime minister who had died by his own hand. He knew that Spiro was bent on discovering what had in this case *déclenché* the dictator's paranoia. He knew that Pëllumb was predicting an imminent day of reckoning, which was only being brought closer by the dictator himself, who was murdering and imprisoning those who were murderers themselves.

I asked Edip what he thought of the Don's version, that predicted that Edip and his colleagues might be rehabilitated. He smiled in the same way as when I had told him the first version of the purge of his defence minister.

'Have you heard of Yezhov?' he asked me.

'No,' I replied.

'He was the man that Stalin used to carry out what was called the "great purge".'

'And then...?'

'In the end, Stalin sentenced Yezhov to death and stopped the purges, but didn't rehabilitate anybody.'

* * *

In our conversations at this time, Edip told me an old story, which is why I have sat down to write this entire account.

In his calm and gentle voice, with its musicality that lent it depth and credibility, he carried me back to the years immediately after the war. 'It wasn't long after we had come down victoriously from the mountains when one day, they summoned me to one of the Party's newly opened offices. They told me that they had decided to send me with a group of partisan comrades who had completed some sort of schooling in Albania for military studies in the Soviet Union. I left the office in a state of indescribable elation. The Soviet Union was the god that had inspired us. Together with Stalin and the ideal of communism, it made up what you might call our holy trinity: the Father, Son, and Holy Ghost. Going there was like touching God with your hand.

'Very soon they also gave us our travel instructions. We were to go first to Belgrade and set off from there by train for the Soviet Union. In Belgrade we were met by a Soviet officer who would escort us to Moscow. We crossed a good part of the Balkans by train. The state of the railways after the war was appalling. The trains we took were hauled by decrepit locomotives and the carriages barely crawled along the track. But our minds were focused only on the Soviet Union.

'We were young, just turning twenty, and we believed in communism with the blind fervour of youth. Although we knew that the Soviet Union had gone through a terrible war, we still imagined it as filled with good things. As soon as we arrived there, we said, everything would change.

'While we were travelling through Romania, we stopped at a station to change trains. One of our comrades wandered off. After a while he came back to us with a furious expression.

"What happened?" we asked him.

"Comrades, that Romanian over there insulted the Soviet Union."

We all bristled.

"How? What did he say?"

"I asked him how far it is to the border. Where are you going? he asked me. I said, to the Soviet Union. He looked at me in amazement and said, but why do you boys need to go there? It's pure poverty and misery."

"Which one was it?"

"Him over there."

'He pointed a finger at a man sitting on a station bench. He was an elderly man and I don't know what he was doing at the station. But for us he was an enemy propagandist, a fascist, a reactionary, a bourgeois maggot. We flung ourselves at him, like a pack of wolves that has found its prey. The Romanian couldn't understand why we'd picked on him. Maybe he had some idea when he recognised our friend, but we left him no time to explain or run away. We punched and kicked him, and some beat him with their pistol butts. He fell to the ground in a heap, and still we beat him, trying to outdo each other in the force of our blows, to show which of us loved the Soviet Union most. Nobody stopped us until a Soviet officer came running to find out what was happening.

"What's going on?" asked the officer.

"He insulted the Soviet Union," we replied.

He crouched down beside the motionless Romanian and took hold of his hand to test his pulse.

"He's dead," he said, looking at us in wonder.

"He insulted the Soviet Union!" said our comrade who had pointed us to him.

The officer led us away in silence. It was just after the war. Nobody detained us. We caught our train and continued on our journey.'

* * *

'When we at last entered the Soviet Union, expecting the trains to be smarter and faster, we found them in an even worse state. I can't forget, at the station of the first town where we stopped, a beggar with amputated legs, playing an accordion and giving us a look that broke your heart. We had never dreamed there could be beggars in the Soviet Union. When we entered our first canteen, they offered us a sort of soup in aluminium bowls with spoons bent even worse than the ones in our prison. We looked at each other as if to say: we killed that Romanian.

'But we never spoke openly among ourselves about what had happened, neither in the Soviet Union nor later, after our studies, when I met my friends from that journey. I even thought I had put this incident out of my mind. But then it surfaced one day, I don't know from what deep level of memory, during my investigation.

'One day a young investigator, apparently told by his older colleagues to beat us, for he evidently believed we had wanted to carry out a putsch, battered me to a pulp with his punches and kicks. It was the first time this had happened and I was also shocked. They sent me back to my cell, and I calmed down lying in the coffin, my eyes closed and thinking about what had happened, when suddenly I saw the crumpled body of the Romanian I had kicked and beaten forty years before. And since then, I've remembered that scene of myself battering that Romanian, almost every day.'

* * *

I wanted to ask questions about this story. What had happened inside him after his first disillusionment in the Soviet Union? Had he remained a believer in the system or had he then started on the arduous road of a double life? I wanted to understand the process whereby he and many others like him had changed from supporters of an ideal for which they were ready to give their lives and to kill others, into slaves of the dictator's paranoia. But I hesitated, unsure if he would give me an answer. At that moment the signal clanged, summoning us for roll-call. We each took our place in our own lines. I watched him go to join his friend, with that distinct manner that marked him out from the rest, and I thought, I don't know why, that some of his courtesy had its origin in the story he had just told me.

Ahlem

A hut in the small camp where we had been transferred two years ago served as both the canteen and the television room. Never before had this room been so full or so silent, except for the announcer's voice booming for more than an hour. Nobody added a whisper to the commentary. Nobody made a move to leave.

It was the first time that the entire group of political prisoners from Spaç, including the mine workers and the reserve list, had assembled in that hut hammered together out of planks and rusty sheet iron.

It was a day of national mourning.

Sitting crammed on the rows of stools, we were experiencing something incredible. The dictator, whose death we had longed for with such insistent yearning, to the point that we had come to believe that he would bury us all before he died himself, was finally being laid in earth. The dreamed-of hour had come. Yet, there was no celebration. The atmosphere was so sombre that nobody dared to show the joy they felt. Since the day his death was announced, the spies had reported any prisoner who let fall a word or gesture of pleasure, and he would be taken from the camp and thrown in a punishment cell with no explanation. Some prisoners feared worse.

A lot of policemen had claimed the first row of stools in front of the screen, and others stood in the corners of the room, their grim presence stifling any possible expression of feeling. When we caught the glance of a friend, we averted our eyes at once, in case some guard or spy caught us. The room was filled with rows of profiles like masks, staring at the black and white screen. More than anything else, the eyes behind these human masks showed a fear of reprisals, mixed with amazement and curiosity at the funeral ceremony.

The coffin on the gun carriage finally entered the Martyrs' Cemetery.

'The commander has come. He is joining his comrades-in-arms!' The commentator's voice rose even higher.

The gun carriage halted by the newly-dug grave, next to the Mother Albania monument. There were people clustering round. The dictator's widow embraced her son. The coffin passed through a number of hands, and remained for a moment in the air, suspended on the ropes that were to lower it to the bottom of the hole. We held our breath.

At that exact moment, a trembling voice echoed from the back of the room.

'Stand up! The greatest man of the nation is being buried!'

We were all on the verge of standing, even the policemen. Then we recognised Ahlem's voice.

We remained seated, but nobody dared to laugh at the madman.

The first spadefuls of earth were thrown on the dictator's coffin.

* * *

Ahlem came to Spaç in 1979. At that time, he was about forty years old, tall, handsome, a man in his prime. Even his savagely cropped hair suited him. He spoke in a quiet and measured voice, courteous and articulate, a rare thing in the camp. He often talked about the political persecution of his family and the large quantities of gold they had possessed at the end of the war. He told the prisoners that he chatted to most that when in freedom he had been very fond of good living, and he was proud of never being short of money even under socialism. He had found ways to earn a little bit more than others. 'Through honest work,' he would emphasise.

When he walked past the policemen who were the camp's internal guards or the chiefs of the Re-education Council, Ahlem used to salute them with a sort of special deference. This meant that rebellious prisoners developed an aversion to him, although he was very polite to them too.

Ahlem was assigned to an underground work brigade on the first monthly schedule after his arrival at the camp. He claimed that he suffered from heart disease and couldn't work in the mines. As a result, they sent him to a punishment cell. He came out a month later, and apparently had arranged not to be sent underground. He didn't appear on the underground roster or on the list of surface workers for two or three months. Finally, somebody remembered him and ordered him below ground. Again, he refused. He resisted with the same calm courtesy with which he told the stories about his life in freedom. Besides mentioning his heart complaint, he told the guard officer that he had never been hostile to the power of the people.

They sent him to a punishment cell again.

When he came out, they left him in the unemployed brigade for a while, and then one day he suddenly disappeared from the camp. A staff car came from the Internal Affairs

Branch of his home town to fetch him. Many people didn't like to think that Ahlem could be a spy, and had gone to do service in the interrogation cells of his local prison. Perhaps he'd really gone to give some explanation demanded by the investigator, or to divorce his wife. But other people began to believe a prisoner from the same town, who said that Ahlem had counterfeited currency and should be viewed with suspicion.

We would be able to tell why he'd been taken away in the GAZ staff car by the length of time he spent in the cells. Anyone sent to spy on other prisoners would stay a long time, sometimes more than a year, because they would be infiltrated mainly to snoop on people whose cases were complicated and those who were being tried in groups on several charges. These trials lasted longer than individual ones. People who were taken away from the camp to provide some explanation or for a divorce came back within a month.

Ahlem stayed away a long time.

It never became clear whether he started to ply his trade in order to save himself from the mine, or he'd been working as a spy even when they put him in the camp's punishment cells.

He returned after several months in the cells with all the appearance of a man who has been kept out of the sun for a long time: with white, delicate skin that in places looked as if it had been peeled away. He was clearly depressed. He spoke very little, and he often wore a distant expression. Someone spread a rumour that he was depressed because the man he had denounced had been shot. Others claimed that he had learned in the cells of his home town that his wife had found another man.

He was assigned to the unemployed brigade. No one expected him now to be sent down for mine work. He entered fully into the brigade's activities, but gradually became slower in his speech and clumsier in his movements. Yet nobody imagined that he could ever go as far as he did.

One day, Ahlem left the first hour of readings from the *Works* of the dictator, climbed up to the rooftop, which was not allowed, jumped over the iron railing, and threw himself into the forbidden zone, heading straight for the soldier in his watchtower. The decent Lazër, one of the internal guards, shouted to the soldier, 'Don't shoot him! Don't shoot him!' But the soldier had used up his single cry of 'Halt!' and let fly a hail of automatic rifle fire. Ahlem collapsed in a heap, and lay huddled. Policemen immediately flooded into the camp. They sent all the prisoners to the dormitories and ordered them not to leave. At first it was thought that Ahlem had been killed, but it turned out that the soldier had shot him in the leg.

A few hours later, they sent him to the hospital.

* * *

Ahlem returned from the hospital suspended between two crutches and in a very bad state. The bullet had shattered his shinbone. However, his psychological condition was even worse. He was almost completely mute. Although he was not paralysed, he took to his bed and began not only to eat there, but to perform all his bodily functions. He pissed regularly on the mattress, and sometimes shat there. He was restrained from this, not by any inhibition, but because his roommates stood on alert to prevent him stinking up the cell. The area round his bunk began to smell worse than the latrine.

The appalling stench led to the daily deterioration of his relations with his cellmates, even though they were initially sympathetic. The prisoners demanded that he be taken to the infirmary or sent back to the hospital, but the authorities paid no attention. No prisoner could have his own room, and the military doctor said that he had come from the hospital with the note, 'cured'. Then rumours began to spread that Ahlem was malingering in the hope that, if he persisted, he would be transferred to the old men's camp at Ballsh, which was close to the town where his family lived. One person said that he had caught him with a cunning look. Someone else said that on coming back from roll-call he had seen him jerking off. His past as a cell spy began to count against him more and more, even though it was remorse at whatever he had done that had led to his attempted suicide.

Soon the first catcalls and insults started coming his way. Nevertheless, Ahlem remained as uncommunicative as before. He never responded to the insults, just as he never thanked anybody, even with a look, for the services performed for him. Nobody would sleep next to him. But the authorities did not want to leave empty beds. Some prisoners insisted that he fouled his bed on purpose just to foul up other people's lives.

Then they sent one of the prisoners from Ahlem's room to the punishment cells twice in a row. He was always cursing the commander, accusing him of leaving Ahlem with them on purpose just to add to their sufferings. When he came out after the second time, he said that he had realized from a mocking remark dropped by the guard that Ahlem must have spied on him. Then even those few who still felt sorry for Ahlem began to cool towards him.

As the hostility towards him deepened, the authorities finally allowed his bed to be shifted to a corner of the room, where it was surrounded by a kind of tent of blankets.

Ahlem lived inside that tent for a long time, for almost as long as he had been in the cells, with the help of what little attention could be given to a sick man in such a place.

* * *

When winter was over, Ahlem left his bed and turned up with his stew bowl in the lines of the unemployed. He had undergone an extraordinary transformation. He limped badly on his injured leg, which had become visibly shorter than the other. He ate stew from the pot with unprecedented greed and within a short time grew disgustingly fat round his buttocks, neck, and face.

He spoke to his fellow-prisoners with the same courtesy as before. But he not only refused to explain in any way his suicide attempt and the subsequent trauma, but said that he could not remember anything of what had happened.

Ahlem's peculiar love for the dictator first became apparent during the two hours of study, that same session from which he had run out in order to kill himself. These hours were very boring, and the prisoners often passed the time whispering, whenever the guards went away. Ahlem began to interrupt more and more often. 'Please shut up. Some of us like these books.'

After a time, he attached to himself a young boy, a prisoner who had arrived recently, sentenced for trying to flee the country. He tried to protect him from all the camp predators, but especially from enemies of the people who might poison him with propaganda. Nobody could tell whether he was really trying to look after him, or whether he had his own predatory intentions. Ahlem did everything for him. He waited for him to return from work with dishes he cooked for him in the private kitchen. He washed and brushed his clothes. He gave him the dictator's books to read. Somebody said that he had heard him tell the boy that in Arabic the world *ahlem* means hope, and that he, and these books, would keep the boy's hope of release alive.

Nobody knew what feelings Ahmet had experienced at that moment when he had stood up in the reading room and rushed out to die. He insisted that he remembered nothing about it. But this room – perhaps not accidentally – became the place where he needed to show his love for the dictator and make amends for what he had done a few years previously, when his action might have been interpreted as an unforgivable insult to the dictator, indicating that he would rather die than sit listening to what the leader had written. At the beginning of the eighties, this room became not only the canteen and reading room but also the television room. The prisoners began to follow international football with the greatest enthusiasm. There was tremendous uproar at one final won by Germany. A few days later, the chief of the Interior Ministry Branch of the district paid one of his occasional visits. He attended one of the meetings that the authorities organized with the aim of encouraging plan fulfilment in the mines. He also spoke himself, providing a survey of the healthy political situation in the country.

After the speech by the chief, several of the brigade leaders among the prisoners stood up, as usual on such occasions. They promised even higher levels of plan fulfilment and made a few material requests. The great mass of prisoners listened sullenly, showing clearly that they were present for the same reason as they went to work – by force.

At the end of the meeting, Ahlem unexpectedly stood up and asked the branch chief if he could add a few words.

Everybody waited to hear what he would say. He turned to the prisoners in the hall, and said, 'I want to make an appeal to you all. Shout "hurrah!" for the party and its glorious leader Enver Hoxha with one half of the enthusiasm you showed when Germany scored a goal.'

A silence followed. Both the prisoners and guards were surprised. None of the commander's men could reproach him for what he said, but they also did not like to hear silences of this kind in response to an appeal that anywhere else in Albania would bring people cheering to their feet.

* * *

From that day, the wretched Ahlem was classed in the special category of accomplices of the commander. These were in general 'normal' sorts of people, who would never admit that they were spies. When they obtained some privileged job, they said that they had got it through a friend. Sometimes they would give no explanation at all. Only rarely did any of them confess, even to an intimate circle, that they were serving the authorities, to gain release or to avoid a second sentence. At any rate, not one of them would ever shout something that was a provocation both to the prisoners and to the authorities.

On the day after the visit of the branch chairman, while Ahlem was limping down to the lavatory, somebody threw a rotten tomato at him. It split open against his backside, which had grown twice as broad as his shoulders. He turned round slowly with a long-suffering expression, looked about, and then continued to descend the stairway in the same abject manner.

As time passed, Ahlem became more and more devoted to the regime that had crippled him. The more his love increased, the more curious the other prisoners became. They would ask about the accident, and Ahlem always replied that he couldn't remember. When anybody insisted on reminding him, he replied coldly that he had heard this story from other people too, but, if it was true, he held it to be the most shameful thing that he'd ever done. He had never wanted such a thing to happen, and he couldn't say why it had taken place. He also no longer told his old stories about his family's prosperity and the wealth he had managed to create for himself. He never mentioned his family at all. His life had frozen at that terrible moment when his leg was smashed in a hail of gunfire. Then, in the dark months that followed, a new Ahlem took shape.

* * *

Life in the camp gradually returned to normal in the weeks after the burial of the dictator. The fears of reprisals faded, and hopes of political changes began to sprout. The prisoners began to taunt and make fun of those who, out of fear of being shot, had signed the telegram of condolences addressed to the dictator's family. This telegram had been read out in the television room in absolute silence, under the pressure of fear. It was now obvious that the initiative for this telegram had not come from above, with the idea of winkling out a few sworn enemies, but from a few collaborators who worked in the Re-education Council.

The irony was that the 'non-signatories' included Ahlem. But unlike those who had refused to sign out of shame, Ahlem had said he couldn't associate his name with a bunch of hypocrites. Instead, he handed in his own long and personal telegram to the commander.

The signatories of the group telegram wanted to forget the whole matter, but Ahlem stubbornly continued his mourning rituals. In one of the open spaces of the camp, there was a large display stand showing the results of contests in socialist emulation, and on one panel there was a photograph of Enver Hoxha. Ahlem found somewhere a broken light fixture and every morning he filled it with fresh water and added a few sunflowers he picked in some untrodden corner of the camp yard. He hung the light fixture under the photograph of the dictator and would sit on a step near the bridge which the senior staff officers would cross as they entered the camp. He sat hanging his head almost all day. Obviously, he'd chosen that position near the entrance and under the display stand in order to parade his grief for the officers to see. But why? It was simulated, said some, but no, he really felt this way, said others.

One day the local police chief came to the camp. Ahlem stood up and said that he wanted a favour.

'What sort of favour?' the chief asked.

'I want a car to go somewhere.'

'Where?' the chief asked.

'To the Martyrs' Cemetery. I want to lay a wreath on the grave of the greatest man of the nation.'

The chief made no reply and continued on his way. He, like the rest of us, wasn't sure whether this was some madman who meant what he said, or was he trying to hoodwink us all?

The determination and self-absorption with which he continued to demonstrate his love for the state and the dictator finally disarmed even those who were most suspicious of him. Even they finally had to admit that this was something other than a sham. The prisoner from his home town who had first spread the rumour of his forgeries said that Ahlem had displayed this type of insanity before: he had refused to admit that the forged money found on him was not original, and insisted until the end that it was money earned with the sweat of his brow. But most connected his madness to his suicide attempt.

Meanwhile, Ahlem's everyday behaviour in the camp remained very polite and proper. He kept up his close friendship with the young boy, to whom some homosexuals had given the nickname 'the Japanese girl'. Ahlem would take books out of the library for him. He never gave anyone any trouble.

* * *

Towards the end of December news reached the camp that there might be an amnesty on Republic Day, 11th January. Different sources confirmed the report, which became more and more credible. This time, we expected a different sort of amnesty, not like the one declared a few years before. At that time, the dictator had released very few political prisoners, with a few cunning exceptions, and had freed recent arrivals, not those who had served the longest time. But now the dictator's successor was expected to show the first signs of clemency.

As Republic Day drew nearer, the amnesty filled our minds more and more, and our anxiety increased. Each prisoner imagined that he might be released. Anybody who received a visit from a relative was pumped for the latest news. Any encouraging news spread through the camp like wildfire. If anyone's visitor had no news to report, or only something meagre, this was ignored as if the visit had never happened. It was as if the Don, the prophet of our release, were present in spirit, although he was now in a different camp.

In this atmosphere, even the most rebellious prisoners started talking to the collaborators, who had contact with the guards and officers and might have picked up some information. But nothing was certain. The rumours took many forms. Some prisoners believed there would be no amnesty at all, while others predicted a general amnesty that would empty the camp.

There was no need for a wake-up call from the crier on the morning of 11th January because most prisoners had spent a sleepless night. We climbed out of our bunks, our ears pricked for the loudspeakers. At six in the morning, the radio's press review announced that the amnesty decree had been published in the main newspapers. The cheers that greeted this news woke up those few prisoners who had fallen asleep towards dawn.

However, the newspapers did not arrive at their usual time, after morning roll-call. Nobody could explain this. The optimists took it for a good sign, but the pessimists for a bad one.

The newspapers didn't arrive until midday. The guard officer brought them, escorted by several more policemen than usual. Before the roll-call began, the officer told the prisoners not to disperse afterwards, but to assemble on the square, because he would read out the decree of the Presidium of the People's Assembly.

The long-awaited moment had arrived at last. The officer climbed up to the highest point overlooking the field, unfolded the newspaper, and began to read the decree line by line, clause by clause. The first article excluded from the amnesty one category of prisoner, the next article another, and another, until it was clear that only a handful were left to be released – prisoners with less than one year of their sentences to serve, or with very light sentences in the first place. Almost all of us would be left inside. So this was why the newspapers had arrived so late.

The officer finished reading and left the camp, escorted by a squad of policemen. We were all stunned, and for a moment no one moved. The few who would be released didn't dare to speak. It was as if the officer had read out a decree adding ten years to everybody's sentences.

Just then, when we were all sunk into a deep despair mixed with hatred, a strong, deep voice came from the back of the crowd.

'Long live the party and the teachings of its immortal leader!'

It was Ahlem.

Nobody had the spirit to laugh at him, or even to grab his crutch and break it over his head. At that moment, his survival mechanism had made him stronger than any of us. He was the first to detach himself from the cowed mass, limping away with his usual shuffle, supported by his crutch.

Frano and Josif

'You shouldn't wonder that we're in prison.'

I stared at him, but said nothing, expecting his explanation. He too stared at me with those of eyes of his that until that day had seemed like the closed double gates to a gloomy house that I dimly remembered from childhood. Now it appeared to me that those gates were open and an unfamiliar light had been struck in the darkness behind them.

'When God created the Universe,' he went on, 'The Devil went to him and said, this whole Universe is yours. Do me a favour and give me that little Earth with those creatures you have put there. God thought a little and replied, "All right, I'll give it to you. But understand that I will have my people there too."'

He paused a moment, as if to make sure I'd properly understood what he said, and added,

'And so, in this world of ours there are so many of the Devil's people and so few of God's.'

I don't know whose hand it was that put my bed in the last hut, No.9, when I was transferred to the camp at Ballsh. It was called the old men's hut because most of the prisoners there were over sixty. I was not yet thirty. But the whims of this hand didn't stop there, but inserted the bed of a son of atheists, who believed in evolution and not in creation, between the bed of a Catholic priest called Frano and that of Josif, the only Protestant in the camp.

It was Josif who, a few days after I had met him, and assuming my unbelief, had explained to me his faith and given me this explanation of our origin and the roots of the evil that we were suffering.

'So we belong to the Devil,' I said to him, laughing.

'Not all of us,' he replied with an expression that made me think that according to him I might be the Devil's, if I laughed like that, but he himself wasn't.

* * *

In earlier years there hadn't been enough elderly men to fill an entire hut. The camp had been built to exploit prison labour to build a refinery for the oil extracted locally. The refinery had come into use a few years ago. It stood opposite the hill of the camp, and its tall chimneys belched smoke and flame incessantly. When the wind blew towards us it brought the heavy stench of the gases the refinery released.

The prisoners had expected to be moved to another project somewhere else. But the completion of the refinery coincided with the wave of purges of hostile groups that the dictator undertook in the mid-1970s. This campaign trebled the prison population and affected all ages. So Ballsh became the camp were most prisoners unable to work in the mine were sent, while most of the young people there, like myself, had been given second sentences while in Spaç.

Like in other huts, in No. 9 too the straw pallets were laid on two levels, in two rows with an aisle between them. The upper level was created by a platform of planks. But

No. 9 had its special characteristics. The lower level was occupied by a number of prisoners who couldn't get up for roll-call because they were very aged and frail, or suffered from serious illnesses. When roll-call came, the duty guard would enter and count them inside. The hut was also several metres shorter than the others, because a separate section had been created at the end, with its own entrance from outside. This section accommodated the terminally ill, who could no longer be left even on the lower level of bunks. Some people called it the porch of death.

Frano, Josif and I had our pallets on the upper level, which was for prisoners who were healthier, despite their age. We were positioned halfway down the room, beside the windowless wall. We climbed up there on wooden steps that were fixed to the planks of the platform every two or three metres, to the side of the aisle.

Frano the priest had just turned sixty, and was a large-framed, stout and ruddy man who kept his trousers up with braces. When he climbed up to his bed it was as if the planks of the entire platform creaked from his bulk and strength. He'd been in prison for eleven years. Like many priests, he'd been accused of being a Vatican spy at the time of the campaign to ban religion and destroy the churches and mosques. They had sentenced him to death, and then reprieved him. He was a man of books and had worked not only as a parish priest but as an associate of the Institute of History. He always kept his reading glasses hanging on his chest by a thin leather thong, stained from the folds of his fleshy neck.

Josif was about seventy, thin and with a lined face. His arthritis made it very difficult for him to climb the steps. He had trained as a dentist in Istanbul before World War Two and had been able to make a living with his profession. He had also served two years in prison in the fifties for refusing his summons to the army, because his religion forbade it. In Ballsh, he had served seven years of a twelve-year sentence for attempting to escape. When I asked him why he had tried to escape at such an age he told me it was a long story and he would explain to me one day.

* * *

'God does not strike bargains with the Devil and does not abandon any of his creatures,' Frano told me one day after I told him about my conversation with Josif. 'Jesus said, the last shall be first. You should know that even the most serious sins can be wiped away with confession and repentance.'

He explained to me that what Josif had been talking about was part of the Protestant doctrine of predestination, which Catholics didn't accept. But he said that Josif was also adding something from his own imagination when he described God's bargain with the Devil.

'But how do you Catholics explain what has happened to us?' I asked him. 'If God sees us and judges our deeds, how can He allow this sort of injustice? Look, how can they keep in prison old men of ninety who can't even move, paralysed people, people who have suffered heart attacks or have cancer? What is God waiting for? Why doesn't He release them from their suffering?'

'You should understand,' he said, becoming even more serious, 'that God doesn't allow any evil to happen except with the aim of drawing good out of it.'

'So the dictator is God's instrument of good?'

'No. God allows evil to happen, as He did when He allowed them to crucify His Son. But He is not the one who orders men to do evil. He has given men freedom to choose. "This man, who was put into your power by the deliberate intention and foreknowledge of God, you took and had crucified by men outside the law." Paul says of Jesus. Do you know the story of Josif and where our neighbour's name comes from? Joseph's brothers wanted to throw him into a well, but then sold him as a slave for twenty shekels and sent his father Jacob a bloodstained coat and said that a wolf had eaten him. Then Joseph spent seven years in prison because of a woman's slander. God didn't instruct these people to harm Joseph. And don't take this Josif of ours too seriously, because he has a screw loose. Do you know how he ended up in prison?'

'No,' I said.

'Because he claimed to have found a cure for cancer.'

'Ah, so he's the famous friend of Shuaip?'

* * *

Even in freedom in Tirana I had heard something about the strange story of two people being sent to prison after finding a cure for cancer. News had travelled among circles of people who dared to talk against the regime that the two geniuses were unable to follow up their discovery because of the dubious political background of their families.

I had asked about them in the camp at Spaç. The prisoners there didn't know Josif's name but remembered the story for the bitter taste left behind by the other inventor, a nurse called Shuaip. They said he was a fraud, a swindler even in prison, who had hoodwinked a good man who happened to be naïve and a bit mad. He had defrauded him of money, persuading him to help bring to fruition his discovery of a cancer cure.

But the story remained unfinished, because some people started enumerating the different sorts of cancer which, they said, made it impossible to invent a single medicine for them all. Other people recalled Shuaip's deceptions in his role as a nurse at Spaç, from where he was released after only three years in prison... Someone more knowledgeable butted in to say that Shuaip wasn't a fraudster but a fantasist, and there was a big difference between an ordinary swindler and a fantasist because the latter deceived himself too. Shuaip himself believed that he'd found the cure for cancer. There was no other way of explaining that instead of gaining money he'd ended up in prison.

Some people hated Shuaip so much that they didn't believe the story of his discovery at all. They claimed that Shuaip had dreamt it up so he would appear insane, to save himself from a sentence for escape. If they had known Josif, the latter group would have abandoned this theory.

* * *

One day Josif took from his pocket some black-and-white photographs and handed them to me. I expected to see pictures of his family, but these were something else. I saw a sequence of strange close-up portraits with stony expressions, of the kind often seen on identity cards, but on whose faces something like black lumps or blotches had spread over the skin. I felt revulsion. I raised my head and looked Josif in the eye to ask what this meant. Josif was satisfied with the feeling I had expressed, and handed to me some other photos with normal faces, but the same stony expression in front of the camera.

'What do these photos mean?' I asked.

'Don't you understand? The first are pictures of people with skin cancer. The second show them after being cured. And they were cured by the medicine invented by a friend of mine with my help. That's why I'm in prison today.'

I looked at the pictures again and saw that they were indeed the same faces. I returned them silently to Josif.

He went on to tell me about his sentence. In the 1960s, he had got to know Shuaip, who had come to him for dental treatment. Shuaip had told him about this discovery, which he had been unable to develop, and complained that this research needed money, while he himself could barely put food on his table. After two appointments, they became such close friends that Josif promised to help him find the funds he needed. He had put some money to one side and had no family to support for he was unmarried.

'But what sort of medicine is it?' I asked.

He told me that it was a complicated formula, a mixture of liquid chemicals, which of course he couldn't reveal to me. He said that after many experiments that he'd documented, he too had become certain of the effect of the medicine and had written to the health minister. The minister's secretary replied in a letter asking them simply to come and give them the formula. They claimed to have made an earth-shattering discovery, yet the minister would not even deign to meet them. They decided they wouldn't simply hand over the formula to these people who shamelessly wanted to appropriate their work. It wasn't a question of money, but of reputation and dignity. It should be known who the inventors were.

Josif told me that after a second and third attempt, to which the Ministry responded merely with silence, they decided to escape and take the formula abroad. But the escape remained merely a plan because they were denounced by an acquaintance whom they had met several times to obtain information about the border.

And so one day the two were put in handcuffs and thrown into solitary prison cells, accused of treachery to the homeland. Josif was sentenced to twelve years as the head of the group, but also as a repeat offender.

'But these are the Devil's people, why did you turn to them with the formula of your medicine?' I asked Josif.

'God knows,' he replied curtly.

I didn't provoke him any further. Josif was a very reticent man and didn't like jokes, especially because he understood that jokes of this kind were made by people who didn't believe in his discovery.

I never told him that I didn't believe in his discovery either, but one day broached the subject again. I was asking to borrow a cupful of sugar and I saw that he was giving me a heaped quantity, so much that I asked him why. He said that this is what his religion taught him.

'So why didn't you hand over your discovery for free, without worrying about your name?' I couldn't resist asking him as we both left the food store.

'I wanted to, but Shuaip wouldn't agree,' he replied.

'And didn't the investigators ask for it?'

'Yes, but I didn't tell them after what they did.'

'And didn't Shuaip give it to them?'

'I don't believe so.'

When we went back to the hut, he picked up from the head of his bed the tin where he kept his photographs, took out a folded letter and gave it to me. '

'I still haven't given up the idea of working together with them. Just look.'

He didn't want to put the letter in my hand, but unfolded it and showed me the header. The address in capital letters was TO THE PRIME MINISTER AND THE HEALTH MINISTER. He said that this was a copy of a letter he'd sent from prison before the death of the Chinese prime minister Zhou Enlai, when the news reached the camp that he was ill with cancer. Josif had offered the formula for his medicine, but received no answer. He closed the subject, telling me the health minister was a criminal.

* * *

When I asked Frano why he thought that Josif hadn't disclosed his formula, he told me that he should have done if he was a true believer. But Protestants, he added, are hypocrites. They claim that God doesn't ask what deeds men commit on earth, because he has his chosen ones, yet they still do all they can, with their deeds, to join the elect. All of Josif's persistence with this discovery can be explained, Frano claimed, by this hypocrisy.

'The truth is that God sees us, judges us, and chooses us on the basis of our deeds. But he doesn't close the door on those who want to turn away from the path of evil, because they always have time to repent and do good.'

'But doesn't forgiving sins solely on the grounds of one confession also encourage hypocrisy in sinners?'

'Obviously you're someone who doesn't believe in the next world. Anyone who believes in God and in the world to come knows that this world is temporary and insignificant in comparison. If he chooses evil, a believer knows that if he doesn't repent he will end up in Hell, while someone who doesn't believe in either Heaven or Hell finds it easier to sin without repenting.'

'But what good does God extract from our sufferings?' I asked, for this question of mine had remained unanswered.

'We are that form of good when we endure our sufferings without losing our faith. It is suffering that lifts us towards God. God became man, came down to earth, and suffered, so that man could become worthy of God.'

'But doesn't God also see that innocent suffering can also deter us from believing in Him? When even Jesus himself lamented on the cross that God had forsaken him, what can we do?'

'But after three days he rose again. That is the lesson we draw from the sufferings of God who became man.'

After all these conversations, I remained firm in my belief that God and the Devil are metaphors that human beings have created to explain themselves and their strange adventures on Earth, and the good and evil inside themselves. Yet their explanations of these things are insufficient, leaving us full of doubts. Sometimes, as a metaphor, Josif's version seemed more truthful and coherent. If power on Earth were in the Devil's hands, then it becomes easier to provide a convincing explanation of the triumph of evil in this world than through convoluted promises of a heavenly paradise reached through sufferings in this earthly life. Yet when I thought it through again, I found that this metaphor didn't explain what the people that Josif called God's flock were looking for on the Devil's Earth, or even why there should be any good at all in this world that had been set aside as the kingdom of evil.

One day as if reading my mind, Frano drew me aside and in a lower voice than usual said, 'Paul writes in his first letter that Christ will soon return, in his own lifetime, to punish the wicked and carry the righteous to God's kingdom. But in his second letter he corrects this. The wicked will continue to rule until the greatest evil of all appears, the son of the Devil. Only then will the Son of God come down.'

* * *

The morning timetable provided for two hours' reading from the dictator's *Works*, with a quarter of an hour's break in the middle. During this ordeal, everybody had to sit on their backsides on their pallets listening to the hut loud-speaker, without occupying themselves with anything else. Only the sick prisoners on the lower level could remain lying down. Anybody who dared to open a book or tried to do something else ended up in a punishment cell.

Few prisoners concentrated on what the reader was saying. For most people, these two hours were a time when the mind grazed at will on the pastureland of the imagina-tion, mostly wandering to our families or life in freedom. Yet even this favourite pasture, frequented every day, be-came tedious. The imagination would go in search of an alternative field. But there was no point in trying to force it into some new meadow, for the imagination is a creature that strays untethered and pauses where it wills.

For a while, after my conversations with Josif and Frano, my imagination found plenty to graze upon. While pretending to listen to the reading, I would watch the prisoners on the platform opposite and play a game, working out where their place would be in the next world. I knew the stories of some of them, and the remainder I judged according to their attitude.

The prisoner I liked best to play this game with was Zenun, whose bed was almost opposite my own. He was a prisoner of about sixty with a sharp-featured, deeply-lined face. During the readings, he would often be seized by a nervous tic. He would abruptly raise his head slightly to one side, and this would be accompanied by a slight, involuntary smile. When people first mentioned him to me, they said that if you hadn't been introduced to him you shouldn't look him in the eye, because he took a direct stare as a provocation and challenge. I had heard that dogs consider straight looks in the eye as a challenge, but this was evidence that this isn't true only for animals, but humans too. During the readings, until the day when we were introduced, I occasionally glanced sidelong at Zenun, but I never caught him looking me in the eye.

Zenun had more quarrels and fights with his fellow-inmates than any other prisoner. When he was young, he had confronted them face to face with fists, knives, or tools such as pick-axes and spades. Now that he was old and weak it was easier for him to spark off a quarrel with sharp words, but he had no strength left and he would be beaten up. However, anyone who beat him would come to grief because Zenun wouldn't sleep until he took his revenge and drew blood. His most recent act of revenge had been in Burrel prison. A muscular prisoner had offended him and told him to shut his mouth. 'And who are you to speak like that to me?' Zenun had retorted. The other prisoner had given him a gentle slap in the face, to remind him not to go any further or he would reach for a stick. Zenun hadn't reacted because the other man was very strong. He had swallowed this humiliation temporarily, intending to spew it back as soon as possible. Before long Zenun got up one night when the other prisoner was asleep, took hold of the brazier where the prisoners burned paper for a little warmth, and threw it in the man's face. The prisoner's eyes were saved, but his left eye socket, struck by the leg of the brazier, was left with a disfiguring scar.

If it is as Josif says, I thought, Zenun may go to paradise because only God knows his final destiny. If it is as Frano says, then he has a chance if he repents and asks for forgiveness before his last day. But Zenun was clearly not afraid of what awaited him in the next world.

His behaviour on this earth was dictated by another sacred book: the Canon of Lekë Dukagjin, the primitive law code of the mountains. Its principles, passed down the generations by word of mouth among the elders of the highlands, were the millstone round his neck. Whenever any dispute arose, according to these principles he would bristle and tell himself: you will be humiliated. You won't be a man any more. If you don't take revenge on the man who hit you, it you don't draw blood, they will pass you your coffee under the knee, the traditional gesture of contempt.

Anybody who messed with Zenun should know that Zenun would be lying in wait for him to strike his head with a stone or some blunt object, to restore his lost honour.

* * *

The imaginative game of speculating on Zenun's fate in the next world was interrupted one day when they brought another prisoner to the upper storey of bunks in Hut No. 9. Whenever I saw him, I wondered whether he was wearing a cross like Frano in the name of God made man or as a victim of the people of the Devil, like Josif.

I had heard Vangjush's name already in Spaç, when the prison van had brought his friend Kiço, with the strange surname of Venediku. Kiço told me that three of them had been arrested, himself with Vangjush, the famous painter from Korça, and Gaqo, the son of the first book publisher in the history of the city. This had been after some posters hostile to the dictator had appeared on the walls of some of the Korça back streets. Kiço himself was unable to say if these posters were the reason for the reprisals or if they had been distributed on purpose by the *Sigurimi*, as a pretext for them. Certainly, these three had no connection with the incident, because they had been chosen simply as well-known local people, to terrorise the others.

Vangjush had studied painting in Athens and Rome under the monarchy. Kiço was a mathematician and musician, deeply learned in philosophy, and Gaqo was a teacher of literature. All three taught at the city's high school where the students held them in particular esteem.

The three had been held for almost two years in solitary cells, so that they would admit to being spies for some hostile state. Rumours were spread round Korça that they had inspired the poster campaign. Kiço came out of the cell not only with a sentence of twenty-five years, but with a serious case of bulimia. There was no filling him. As soon as the work brigades finished their meals, especially the miners who had the largest bread rations, he would go to the canteen and secretly gobble every crust left on the tables.

Then one day the head of the Maintenance Office, out of sympathy, made him the canteen cleaner. This seemed to alleviate his sufferings from bulimia to some extent, but before long he died suddenly of a heart attack while cleaning the canteen tables.

In Vangjush's case, two years in the investigation cells had also accelerated the development of the terrible disease that seemed to have been lying in wait for him in the darkness of confinement, to appear there and announce to him that his days were numbered. When I first met him in the camp he was in a different hut, but my interest in painting and my acquaintance with some of the artists of the city made us friends. I noticed at once that his hands were shaking. He told me he suffered from Parkinson's disease, which had first shown itself in the cell, and that he took medication sent by his family. He explained to me that this medicine helped to produce dopamine, the neurotransmitter that sends impulses from the brain to the muscles. He knew that the time would come when this medication no longer had any effect, but he hoped that another treatment would arrive.

During this first period of our friendship, he was able to move, and would go out to roll-call. Sometimes after the readings when the weather was good, we would go out for a short walk together round the field. I would give him my arm and we would walk at his slow pace. He talked to me about his new ideas for paintings he would do after his release. He said that until that point he had been too academic but now he had fresh inspiration.

He described his new canvases as having strong colours, used with freedom. He had imagined them in his solitary cell, he said, out of the need to create light in the darkness. Sometimes he crouched down and drew in the earth of the field with some sharp stone he pulled out of the ground. I wondered to see how his forearm then became strong and there was almost no tremor in his hand. Thinking of the dopamine that sent impulses through the channels of the brain down to the arm and hand muscles, I thought that it must be inspiration that at these times generated more dopamine.

He would feel tired after half an hour's walk and ask to go back to his bed. He lay there increasingly often, totally crushed.

He didn't want to be transferred to the lower level of Hut No. 9, but one day he fell down while waiting in line for the guard officer to count him at roll-call. They carried him to the sick bay and, when he came out, moved him to Hut No.9, with the right not to turn up for roll-call.

His family wrote more and more letters to top-level leaders, explaining that he was suffering from an incurable disease and begging for him to be released. After they came for visits, I would ask Kiço if they'd received any replies, but there was nothing.

One day I asked him if he believed in God and in the world to come.

'No,' he said. 'I'm an agnostic, but I believe that art and painting keep my soul alive.'

And he described again his ideas for paintings with the light and colours that he imagined. From his descriptions, especially of the dark backgrounds which exploded into vibrant colours, it seemed to me that they expressed his despairing efforts to banish the darkness of death that drew closer every day.

* * *

The bitterly cold winter at Ballsh was made worse by the damp location.

Waking at five o'clock, we saw the camp covered with a white veil of frost that lasted a long time, for the camp was situated on the northern slope of a hill and it took time for the sun's rays to reach the huts surrounded by barbed wire and watchtowers. Going out into the five o'clock cold and darkness was one of the most difficult moments of the day. After completing their morning routines and tidying their beds the prisoners were not allowed back in the huts. Most gathered in the canteen hall to warm up at least a little from each other's breath as they waited for the morning tea ration. The strongest, wrapped in dingy overcoats, took brisk walks round the field or beside the huts, their breath steaming. Even the soldiers in the watch towers would stamp their feet on the plank floors as they tried to get warm.

The sick prisoners of Hut No. 9 barely moved from their beds in winter. Even during the day, they often lay with their heads buried in blankets, so that their beds resembled piles of rags thrown in random heaps. Some of the guard officers, if they were among those the prisoners considered kind-hearted, didn't even ask them to sit up when they came in to count them.

Winter was also the season when some entered a terminal state and were moved to the porch of death, the only place apart from the Maintenance Office where there was a stove. There they were looked after by Sadik, a taciturn prisoner who barely communicated with others in the camp.

Rumour had it that he, assisted by Galip, the commander's most trusted prisoner, would take the bodies of the dead outside the wire for burial. The place of burial was kept secret. People said there was a plot somewhere behind the hill of the camp, but neither Sadik nor Galip ever talked about it.

These two were never even seen to keep company together in the camp.

Nobody could say with certainty what the legal provisions were for prisoners who died. Some prisoners insisted that the law demanded that they had to complete their sentences before their bones could be given to their families, and so the plot was mapped out, and bottles containing the names of the dead were also buried in the graves. But the oldest prisoners, who had moved with the camp from one construction project to the next, said that there was no question of any graveyard, because, if the camp was relocated every four or five years, as had happened, who would look after a plot of land adjacent to some cement works or refinery, just because it had a few bodies in it? Even if there was a law that promised the disinterment of bodies after the completion of sentences, families would neither dare nor be able to apply for such a thing. Nobody had ever heard of such a case.

Prison was an underground domain where the concept of a grave had no meaning, for it was itself a sort of grave that separated prisoners from the world of the living. And if a grave can be conceived as a place of honour and remembrance, they had been put where they were precisely because they deserved no honour or remembrance. So to die in prison meant only the end of a physical and moral burial that had begun when a prisoner was deprived of freedom and thrust in a cell.

* * *

Vangjush's first winter in Hut No. 9 was a particularly cold one. Nevertheless, he survived the porch of death that winter. When spring arrived, he tried to raise himself several times for a short walk, but after a few excursions he gave up. His legs wouldn't support him. The medication he took to raise his dopamine levels was no longer effective. He asked for other, stronger medication. When this came, he seemed to improve for a while, but this didn't last long.

His hands now trembled even after he took his medication. He left his bed only for the few minutes necessary to go to the toilet, his arm supported by another prisoner who also fed him. This prisoner had slept in a nearby bed in his previous hut. He had no support from his family and had started helping Vangjush at this time. In exchange, Vangjush would give him a portion of his bread ration and the canteen food, because he himself ate very little. He also gave him several packets of cigarettes which his family sent him in their monthly parcels especially for this purpose.

* * *

When summer came with its exhausting heat, filth, and even heavier stench from the refinery chimneys, Vangjush reached the state in which he could no longer lift his arms. One day I was horrified to see a host of flies gather on his face beside the spittle dribbling from his lips. He could no longer wave them away. This soon became his usual situation. Now and then the prisoner who fed him shooed off the flies and wiped the spittle, but the insects returned again and again to his almost motionless face.

When I climbed down the ladder and saw this sight I would often sit down on the end of his bed, get rid of the flies, and start on his favourite topic of conversation: news of the amnesty that his family expected. It was very hard for him to talk, and his stumbling words were impossible to understand. But his moving lips and the sounds he produced by his efforts were still a form of communication. Knowing the subject, I intuited what he wanted to say. 'They've been given a lot of hope,' seemed to be his reply.

Then came the time when I communicated with him only through the eyes. I would sit down and remain there, because I could tell from his eyes that he was glad of this, and ask him this same question, until I noticed that his eyes too were freezing, for he stared fixedly at one spot.

One day, with almost immobile eyes, he tried to tell me something. At that moment the prisoner who fed him arrived, offered me the packet of cigarettes and a toffee brought by Vangjush's family, and said that his relatives were sure this time that he would be released. I don't know if they told him this because they really were hopeful or just to console him.

Now it was clear that if no positive response came soon, he would be moved to the porch of death.

* * *

'One thing I don't understand,' I said to Josif as I climbed up to my bed after visiting Vangjush. 'According to your religion, the Devil's people can never become God's and God's can never become the Devil's – or can they change?'

'No,' he said. 'They can't change. This world belongs to the Devil.'

'So that means that none of the Devil's people can feel mercy and think that Vangjush should be sent to die at home?'

'The Devil is the Devil and knows no goodness or mercy. He gains satisfaction only from doing evil.'

'Then why had God thrown his people into this world of the Devil?'

'To show his power over the Devil.'

'Does God really need to demonstrate his omnipotence to the Devil?'

'Yes, because the Devil tries to challenge him.'

'But didn't God send Jesus to Earth to save humankind?' I asked.

'This is a misunderstanding of the Catholics. Jesus didn't come for everybody, but only to save God's people. Jesus said, 'I pray not for the world but for those you have given me, because they belong to you.'

'But how does he recognise his own? I can say that neither Vangjush nor you or I belong to this flock because Jesus doesn't stretch out his hand to us.'

'You don't understand anything, because you don't believe in the next world. We are here only to show that God's people exist, not to change our lives on this earth. This world belongs to the Devil. What we are living through here seems to you very important, and so you ask for God's hand here, whereas in fact all this is totally insignificant compared to what awaits us.'

Both Josif and Frano limited me to the next world, which I refused even to imagine, let alone believe in. I even found it hard to credit that they believed in it entirely, without a shadow of doubt. Otherwise, why did they make such strenuous efforts to stay alive?

One day when Frano told me how the investigators had forced him to confess to being a Vatican spy to avoid a death sentence, I said to him. 'That would be all well and good for me, because I don't believe in the next world, but why did you confess? Wouldn't death be for you the quickest route to heaven?'

He looked me in the eye and answered briefly, 'Even Jesus before he was crucified went to the Garden of Gethsemane and prayed to his Father, 'Let this cup pass from me.'

I didn't press the point further, but his reply didn't convince me. It strengthened my belief that Jesus was a human being, just like us, and that his cry on the cross, 'Father, why have you forsaken me,' was the tragic disillusionment of a man who realises that there is nothing beyond the world we live in, that we are alone on our journey through it, and that the son of the Devil has visited the earth so often and the Son of God hasn't descended to save us.

* * *

Vangjush too was a man abandoned to the cruel hands of his brethren, without hope of salvation. The question was, why did these brethren behave so cruelly? 'Because they are the Devil's,' Josif told me. 'Because they don't believe in God, who is love,' Frano told me. 'Because they don't fear punishment in the next world,' both of them told me. But according to the *Works* of the dictator, which we read every day, the answer was that these cruelties were perpetrated for the sake of good. They purged the world of swindlers who preached a heavenly paradise in order to justify hell on earth. The *Works* claimed that happiness must be built on Earth and to achieve this the world must be cleansed of people like Frano and Josif who believed in the world to come, and also of people like Vangjush and me, who didn't believe in this promised happiness. Therefore, they didn't consider this lack of mercy towards us a form of cruelty, but a virtue. At least that is how they justified themselves, because it was hard to imagine that the dictator genuinely believed in the paradise that he himself promised. When he preached ruthlessness, it was as if he were trying to convince himself, and his own people, that they should have no doubts in what they were doing. And this need to quell doubts through cruelty stemmed from a fear that they were losing faith in the sole justification for their cruelty, and also from the fear that the countless dead would persuade the living to hold them to account one day for what had been horrible crimes, pure and simple.

* * *

Sometimes when we couldn't sleep, Frano would talk to me about his unfinished life's work. This was a translation from the Latin of *Illyricum Sacrum*, to which he had devoted seven years during his time as a parish priest in a small town in the north.

This work in several volumes described the history of the Catholic Church in the lands of the Western Balkans, then known as Illyria, in whose south our own country was situated. It told of a Venetian, Father Filipo Riceputi, who had sailed down the length of the Adriatic coast, stopping at all the coastal cities. From these ports, he sent helpers into the interior for historical research, and from them he acquired his material. He continued his voyage south, sending his messengers to all the ecclesiastical centres in the mountains along the coast.

Usually, I would listen to Frano without interrupting as he described to me the contents of the different chapters of this translation. I also initially listened in this way as he told me about a cart drawn by oxen, laden with manuscripts, books, and historical objects which testified to the existence of the Church in the depths of our own mountains. This cart, having made its way through all the mud and marshes of the coast, had been drowned while crossing the River Drin and was lost with all its valuable cargo for Father Riceputi.

But Frano described this chapter to me at the time of Vangjush's last agony, which had set my mind running over the origin of the dictator's cruelty. I told Frano that I didn't believe any cargo had been carried from the mountains of the interior. The drowning of the cart must have been a fiction, because no church or gospel, no mosque or Qu'ran had penetrated those mountains from which we had descended. Nothing of this kind could come down from there in the form of books. The idea that we should forgive our enemies, or that he who is without sin should cast the first stone had never reached there. This was the domain of Zenun's Canon, which in place of forgiveness and humility preached blood revenge and pride.

Frano could tell where I was heading. I told him that the first faith to reach this society ruled by the Canon was communism, which prophesied the arrival of paradise on Earth through fire and steel. Only this could explain the cruelty of not releasing sick men like Vangjush. The communists had combined the Canon and their faith. After killing people in the name of this faith, they continued killing enemies and the relatives of enemies because they lived in fear of revenge, and they called this purging society of the remnants of the bourgeoisie.

But Frano didn't accept this connection. He was heir to the tradition of Albanian Catholic priests of the twentieth century, who had blended their Catholic faith with nationalism and considered the Canon a part of their identity.

Frano called communism a result of the denial of God. Whereas, he said, the Canon and his faith had lived together. The Canon should be seen as a tradition rooted in justice. It survives like an animal that emerges from its lair at times of anarchy.

I insisted on my view that the Canon is a sign of primitive society that recognised neither a state nor a religion.

'Look at Zenun,' I said. Zenun was sitting opposite us waiting for the reading to start. 'It's pure chance that he didn't become a communist, the sort that kill without mercy. So many of his kind have become communists.'

In those days Zenun was wearing a black kerchief round his head, and kept his eyes fixed on a single point. It really was one of those times when you shouldn't look him in the eye. Someone had hit him in a quarrel. The kerchief was a sign that his honour had been offended and he wouldn't remove it until he'd taken his revenge. Perhaps he would lie in wait until his enemy was washing his face in the bathroom and then hit him with a stone on the back of his head. Or perhaps it would be when his enemy was squatting over the toilet, or eating his food in the canteen, but the time had to come.

* * *

Autumn was brief that year and winter returned with its morning frost and the bitter cold that drove the prisoners to huddle in the canteen. On one of the coldest days of that winter, after roll-call was over and we returned to the hut for the reading, we found that Vangjush had gone. The prisoners who slept on either side of him went up to his bed, and strangely it seemed as if there had never been anyone there at all.

He had been carried to the porch of death.

It wasn't the first time I'd been in that room. I had visited Murat, a fellow-prisoner of mine in Spaç, a permanent occupant of the room. He was kept there because he had been 'caught in a slide,' as the miners called a rock fall in the mine. He was paralysed from the waist down and needed total care.

The air was warmer because a round tin stove had been lit, of the sort improvised from old oil barrels. I looked around and saw that of the six single-storey beds with metal legs and a metal network of springs, the kind used in hospitals, only those of Vangjush and Murat were occupied.

Vangjush's bed was closest to the stove. Sadik had propped him up on a pillow to give him a little bit of elevation. His eyes were open, but I couldn't tell if he recognised me. I realised that it was no use communicating with those eyes or trying to find any feeling in them, even the fear of death. It seemed that he no longer felt any pain from the paralysis of the body that had gradually crept up on him, without yet reaching his heart. I couldn't imagine what was happening in his mind, but my impression was that his spirit had given up long ago. Only his body still hadn't surrendered.

Then a slight movement of his eyes and his lip signalled that he had recognised me. I sat on the edge of his bed, without speaking.

Sadik went to give an injection to Murat, who growled and snorted, calling those who kept people like him and Vangjush in prison cowards and bastards.

I stayed a while and then said goodbye, because the signal had clanged for the start of the reading.

As the announcer's voice came over the loudspeaker reading a chapter from the dictator's latest *Work*, my mind was still focused on the porch of death and Vangjush's almost total paralysis. I tried to think what form death would take, I looked for a moment at Zenun's black kerchief, but this too I associated with mourning black, not Zenun's revenge.

* * *

Vangjush died at night, two days after my visit.

'They took him away very early in the morning before wake-up and buried him,' Murat told me, pointing to Sadik, when I went to visit him in the porch of death.

Sadik looked me straight in the eyes, in silence, but his expression told me clearly not to ask about the burial, because he couldn't talk about it. I very much wanted to know if they had buried a bottle with his name together with the body.

Immediately after roll-call we went back indoors for the reading of the dictator's *Works*. I told Frano and Josif that Vangjush had died. They took in the news without uttering a word.

During the reading, in my imagination I asked the two where Vangjush had ended up.

'I don't know,' Josif replied. 'God knows.'

'I don't know,' Frano also said, but after a moment's thought he added, 'He too was one of God's sons.' Frano sat a little longer while the announcer droned on, and then he reminded me of Paul's words about Jesus: 'This man who was put into your power by the deliberate intention and foreknowledge of God, you took and had crucified by men outside the law.'

Nuri

First meeting
Tirana, the kaush, 1975

On the day when I first came down from the investigation cells as a newly-sentenced prisoner to the *kaush*, the first prisoner who spoke to me was a stout man of about forty-five, with greying hair. He was extremely short-sighted and wore square-framed glasses with thick lenses. He squeezed my hand firmly in both his own and with a smile that revealed surprisingly even teeth, he introduced himself in the confidence that I would know him.

I immediately remembered hearing Nuri's name and his story. He had been mentioned in our home as the brother of an old family friend, Hamdi, with whom my father had been a communist partisan during the war. The entire family was one of those called 'families from the war,' who were considered pillars of the state. At that time Hamdi was the dictator's first secretary, and his younger brothers enjoyed every privilege, going to study abroad at universities in the East.

But after the break with the Soviet Union, the family's prospects took a turn for the worse. At this time, I heard my father telling my mother with great anxiety that the two younger brothers, Nuri, who had just finished medical studies in Czechoslovakia, and Dullë, whose studies in journalism in Moscow had been interrupted, had been caught at the border while attempting to escape. Their elder brother Hamdi was told that after this he couldn't work alongside the leader.

A few days later I heard that the dictator's wife, who had a special affection for Hamdi, had used her influence to ensure that he wasn't moved from Tirana, but could work as deputy chief editor of the newspaper *Zëri i Popullit,* where my father was chief. This connection through work made Hamdi an even closer friend of the family.

I never heard the two brothers who had tried to escape mentioned again.

* * *

When I met him, Nuri had already spent more than ten years in prison. He was in the *kaush* because they were transferring him to practise his profession as a doctor in another camp. You could tell from his clothes that 'the Doctor', as the prisoners called him, was a long-standing prisoner, because new prisoners like myself still wore their own shoes and civilian clothes, grimy from long periods in the cells, but still of different colours. Nuri had sandals and a thin brown canvas jacket, pale from frequent washing. It didn't take much imagination to see that this was prison issue. He wore trousers of the same material, even more drained of colour, and moccasins in place of shoes.

His face was also ruddier than that of prisoners coming out after long spells in isolation. I took my place to sleep in the bed next to his, and noticed that in contrast to us new arrivals, who had only the straw pallet and the blankets of the *kaush*, he had his own bedsheets with him.

* * *

After the evening soup was served and we finished in the bathroom, the *kaush* seethed with prisoners grouped in conversation. At that time the *kaush* had only two floors, and the majority gathered on the upper one, which made the *kaush* resemble a ship sailing in a sea of tobacco smoke, for most of the prisoners smoked incessantly.

For anyone coming out of the long torture of solitary confinement, it was a real joy to find an acquaintance on the deck of that ship. This pleasure was unbounded when you could quench your thirst for human contact with someone you knew, even distantly or indirectly, with whom you could share memories of people you both knew and loved, and so dearly missed.

That first night I told Nuri the story of my arrest and conviction and we talked at length about the people we both knew: my parents and his brothers. I learned that besides Hamdi and Dullë he also had a brother called Xhavit, who had finished his studies in geology in the Soviet Union and married a Russian, who had remained in Albania with him. He spoke of his brothers with love, but he was worried about Dullë, who was languishing in Burrel prison. Sometimes he swore 'upon Dullë's head'.

The second night, Nuri wanted to talk more than to listen, and we spent even longer together. By midnight, he was telling me the story of his failed escape. He had set off with a group of friends to cross the Yugoslav frontier near Lake Ohrid, but they had been caught before even reaching the border. He also told me about the ten years he had spent in prison so far, and the camps where he done time during all these years.

But from all his stories, what I remembered was the woman to whom he returned again and again, who cast her light over the anxious days of preparation for escape, and over the wretched ten years of life behind barbed wire: this was Vlasta, his Czech fiancée, the reason for his escape attempt and his imprisonment.

* * *

Nuri had completed his studies in Prague at the end of the 1950s. It was there, in 1957, that he had got to know Vlasta. She was a trainee teacher, while Nuri was studying medicine. They had met on a bus. During the summer vacation, Vlasta worked as a conductor on a bus route, and one day Nuri boarded her bus. They chatted only briefly, but she made an impression on Nuri. From that day on, he would wait for her bus to see her sweet smile and dear, deep eyes, from which he could no longer tear himself away.

By the time the college term started, their friendship had deepened into love, and both of them believed they had found their partner for life. They became engaged, and intended to get married after completing their studies.

Then in 1961 came the breach with the Soviet Union and the entire Eastern bloc. Albania broke off all contact with what the leadership, under Enver Hoxha, called 'the revisionist countries', which had condemned Stalinism.

At the time, Nuri was in Tirana, and Vlasta still in Prague. Like many Albanians who were engaged or married to women from the East, he was asked to break off all ties with this foreigner who was now a member of an enemy camp that was just as dangerous as the West, if not more so. By breaking off his engagement, he would also reaffirm his loyalty to the Party and the leadership, with which Nuri's family had been closely tied since the time of the 'National Liberation'. Hamdi tried to persuade him to do this, but in vain. Then the Party Secretary of Tirana had summoned him, to express clearly and officially the organisation's viewpoint. Nuri replied by telling the story about a bird, who, when his mate dies, climbs high into the sky, folds his wings, and falls dead to the ground.

He whispered to me that after this meeting he felt he was put under surveillance. 'But there is no worse torture,' he said, 'than to remain alive after you have lost your soul. When I lost touch with Vlasta, a terrible rift opened up in my life. I was torn between Prague and Tirana. My body walked about in Tirana, but my soul flew away to Prague. Every day my soul deserted me in search of Vlasta. Wherever I was, at home, on the street, in the hospital – Vlasta was on my mind. Then I realised that I would have to do something or I would lose my mind.'

It was love and not politics that led Nuri to join a group that was organising an escape attempt across the Yugoslav border. According to the Criminal Code, which was modelled on Stalin's, this was an act of treason to the homeland punishable by ten years' imprisonment or the death penalty – if you didn't end up shot by a border guard. All the members of the group were captured as soon as they reached the shores of Lake Ohrid. They had probably been betrayed beforehand. They were all sentenced to long prison sentences – Nuri to sixteen years.

He told his story briefly and dryly. These were ordinary stories and prison was full of them. But his eyes began to shine and his tongue loosened as soon as he mentioned Vlasta and how beautiful and sensitive she was, and when he talked about the ring with the green stone, the colour of hope, that he'd given her in 1961, and his last gift of a pair of white shoes. He dwelt at length on the only letter he had received from her, in 1966, when he had been in the Rubik camp. She wrote that she would never forget him, and would wait not sixteen, but fifty years. 'There is no God who will separate me from her,' Nuri said, 'and only when we are together will I put those shoes on her feet.' With these words, he ended his story in the *kaush*.

The next day, the prison van took him away to the camp for ordinary criminals at Borsh, where he was to work as a doctor.

A few days later, I left for the camp at Spaç.

Second Meeting
Ballsh 1979

I met Nuri again five years later in December 1979 in the camp at Ballsh. He had been brought there shortly before me, having been given a second sentence at Borsh. This was the most savage period in the prisons, when second sentences were common. They fell like fatal blows of life imprisonment.

Now we both belonged to the category of reconvicted prisoners who didn't know when they would be released. This created a special closeness in the group, because we all knew that our destiny was predetermined: either we would die in prison, or the dictator would die.

A few days after I arrived, I went for my first walk with Nuri on the big field in front of the camp huts. This time we started our conversation with stories about reconvictions. He told me about his own second sentence, and said that it had happened because of a family tragedy. His brother Xhavit, a former director in the oil industry, had been shot on a charge of sabotage with the 'oil gang', who were convicted in 1976–7. Nuri had lost self-control and spoken out very angrily in the camp about his brother's innocence and his execution, and had been sentenced to a further ten years for agitation and propaganda. I noticed that now, whenever he swore, it was 'upon Xhavit's soul'. He told me that when under investigation this second time, he had suffered much more.

'If I fall into the interrogators' hands again, I won't be able to stand any more,' he said.

* * *

My memories of my first meeting with Nuri were above all of his undying love for Vlasta, and I could hardly wait to ask about this. I thought his eyes would sparkle as soon as he spoke about her, but no. In his wretched mental state after the shooting of his brother and his sufferings under the investigators, he told me something that he had not said five years earlier in the *kaush*.

After that letter he'd received from her in 1966, he managed to send to her, through a Kosovar prisoner who after his release had returned to Yugoslavia, a letter in which he asked her to look after herself, and to find someone to marry, because his own life was finished in the prisons of Albania. I stared at him, amazed, remembering what he had told me in the *kaush*.

But he appeared very clear about what he said.

Such high-minded messages from prisoners to women left outside, urging them to pursue a new destiny, were fraught with ambiguity. Sometimes they were an attempt by the prisoner to banish the tormenting spectre of a woman he loved. They might be the sign of a love that had succeeded in sublimating itself entirely, but they might also be indirect appeals, through an act of self-sacrifice, for these women to continue to love the prisoner and stay faithful to him. As for Nuri, it seemed to me that he had long ago submitted to his fate, and that the message, sent more than ten years ago, perhaps with a different intention at the time, was a sign that his ardour for Vlasta and his hope of meeting her again were now extinguished.

But one day, something surprising happened that showed me that he hadn't given up. As we were taking our usual walk, and talking as always about politics, Nuri gripped me suddenly by the arm and made me stop. Totally concentrated, he told me to keep quiet and listen to the orchestral piece over the camp loudspeaker, which was broadcasting Radio Tirana. 'This is Solveig's Song by Edvard Grieg,' he said. 'Solveig waits for Peer Gynt in a cottage in the middle of the forest, but he doesn't come.' He sang the text in Albanian to the music:

> 'Spring and summer and autumn will pass
> And winter will cover the earth again.
> You will return, I will never forget you
> I gave you my heart in youth.'

He went on holding me firmly by the arm, singing the words to the aria until it ended.

Penelope waiting for Ulysses, Mercedes waiting for Monte Cristo, Solveig waiting for Peer Gynt – these symbols of faithful women waiting for years on end for their husbands or lovers – were characters that prisoners in their imaginations projected onto their wives, fiancées, or lovers left outside. They dreamed of the day of being reunited with them as the best day of their lives.

'So you haven't lost hope,' I said.

'Do you know the story of Peer Gynt?' said Nuri. 'He fell in love with Solveig when he was young, but soon set off travelling throughout the world. He wasted his whole life in escapades and mischief. When his time came to die, the devils told him that he would be thrown into the casting ladle of souls to be melted down, because they had no particular value. He could only save himself if he could show that he had done some great deed, whether good or bad. Peer Gynt started to tell all his wicked exploits, because he had done no good deeds. He told them about the time when his ship was sinking, and to save his own skin he kicked away a seaman who was clinging to the wreckage. The devils said this didn't count, because it was what any man would do. He was losing all hope, but, just when he was not expecting it, a testimony was found that saved his soul: Solveig, now in old age, was still waiting for him with her unending love. 'For me too,' said Nuri, 'there will only be Vlasta's love to show that I did anything in this life.'

I never broached the subject of Vlasta again, and nor did Nuri. We talked about politics and played chess more often, to keep our hopes alive, and to kill time. One summer day we were lying on our bunks playing chess when Nuri was summoned. He was so absorbed in our game that he said to me as he stood up, 'Keep the positions. You're going to lose.' I thought he would come back, but he never returned. A few days later, the news came that he had been arrested again, on account of his loose tongue, always cursing Xhavit's murder. But we were not too upset on his account, because he had so long still to serve that ten years more or less made little difference. He would have time to serve even after his death.

Third meeting
Spaç, 1985

Five more years passed before I met Nuri for the third time, in 1985 in Spaç, where I had been sent back in 1983. I returned after a winter in the camp at Qafë Bari where the youngest prisoners went after the amnesty that led to the closure of Ballsh. They brought Nuri from the camp for ordinary criminals at Batra near Martanesh, where he had worked for several years, because the doctor who had worked in Spaç up till then had been released.

His hair and beard had turned totally white. Even his spectacles had thicker lenses. He had now spent almost twenty years in prison, compared to my eleven.

When I went to his doctor's room he showed me a small tom-cat that he had brought with him, called Çoku. He was a grey tom-cat, a beautiful little tiger, but very wild and stand-offish. Try to stroke him, and he would run off at once. Only Nuri could go near him, and he loved him like a child. He would take Çoku on his lap and point out how he had lost part of one ear. Nuri had cut it off when he was a kitten, and indeed it was after this that they had grown so close. Çoku had wandered uninvited into Nuri's surgery and, confused by the glow of the red-hot wires of the hot plate that Nuri used for heating, had poked his head too close. He could have been electrocuted. Nuri cut off his charred ear and treated him, and from then on, the two were devoted to each other like father and son. 'Daddy's Çoku,' 'Daddy's Çoku' Nuri would murmur continually.

'This is the child that Enver Hoxha has left to me,' he said.

I don't know why I didn't like to ask about Vlasta, but perhaps it was because I saw all his love concentrated on this tom-cat.

Çoku didn't spend long periods with Nuri, partly because of the brutal environment of Spaç, where there were many semi-feral cats that fed themselves on the canteen waste, and partly because of his wild nature. He would run off and vanish during the day, returning only at night. Seeing how much Nuri loved him, I felt sorry for his bad luck in having such a mischievous child. It seemed that for him the best time was at night, when Çoku returned from his escapades outside the camp.

His relationship with Çoku grew stronger and deeper, and the prisoners in Spaç often mentioned it, either in mockery or affection. But often Nuri fell foul of prisoners whose applications for sick leave he had refused, and who said that he gave days off only to those who paid him with tinned food for Çoku. He had the reputation of being a doctor of great integrity in his work, but some said that where Çoku was concerned he too was corruptible. He'd been seen giving Çoku tins of sardines, and some said that he would ask prisoners for these tins in exchange for a day off work down the mine. This accusation was all the more serious, because most of the prisoners never saw sight of a sardine. Other prisoners defended him and said the very opposite was true: that he was very fair in giving leave, because he was scared of being spied on. This was one of the reasons why he had fallen out with some prisoners who were snoops for the authorities, whose relationship with the previous doctor had been a cosy one.

But Nuri had also made enemies of two camp guards who were used to taking medicines from the prison clinic home for their families and friends, which Nuri no longer tolerated. This story seemed the more likely.

The day came when Nuri, in great distress, told his closest friends among the prisoners that Çoku had not come back to him for the last two nights. He asked them if they had seen him. A third night passed, and on the fourth he searched for him everywhere. Then the first rumours started to circulate, that the prisoners who hated Nuri had joined forces with the guards whom he had displeased, and had killed Çoku.

* * *

The cat's disappearance became the event of the day in the whole camp. Nuri, as he gradually realised that something terrible must have happened, was beside himself. Then the truth came to light, but still nobody dared tell Nuri that Çoku had been killed. People even knew where his body was, down by the stream.

One day a prisoner drew me aside and took me to a corner of the camp from where a part of the ravine that fell away from the mine galleries through no man's land. 'Look at that grey thing down there,' he said. That's Çoku.'

What had happened? Nuri's sworn enemies had gone to the clinic during the night, where Çoku slept after his midnight adventures. They caught him and threw him in a barrel of water, slamming down the lid. They held the lid firm until Çoku went still and then they pulled him out, threw him over the barbed wire into the ravine beyond. They had done all this with the understanding of the guard on the night shift.

Finally, Nuri found out. His grief was terrible. He threatened the authorities that he would stop work if he wasn't allowed to go outside the wire to fetch his cat, and the commander gave in, because, as camp doctor, Nuri was indispensable.

Escorted by guards, Nuri went outside and fetched the body, took it to his doctor's surgery and carefully washed away the mud of the stream. He spent a night alongside him, weeping. The next day, he wrapped the cat in white cloth, laid him in a box, and made a request to bury him in no man's land. This disgusted everybody, but his grief was such a distressing sight that again the authorities gave way.

When he went out to bury the cat, he saw a large group of prisoners that had spontaneously gathered in the yard. He burst out in a tirade of hatred against the murderers of his child.

'Heathens! You have no human feelings!' Meanwhile, Dod Miri the storehouse guard, who had collaborated with Çoku's murderers and the guards who had helped them, walked up to Nuri, with a big grin and a bunch of flowers to put on the grave.

'Get lost, scumbag!' howled Nuri.

As he left to bury Çoku in a corner of no man's land, the group of prisoners scattered, some weak with laughter, some hanging their heads.

* * *

A few days later, I found Nuri calmer. I mentioned the subject of Çoku. He showed me a plaster on the back of his right hand. This was one of the last scratches that Çoku had left on him, which he had made deeper with a scalpel to keep the scar as a reminder forever.

'Believe me,' he said. 'For me, losing that cat was like losing a child. I wasn't so upset even when they told me of my mother's death. It was Enver Hoxha's dogs that killed him. Now I have no one left.'

'What about Vlasta?' I asked.

'Vlasta is married,' he said.

'Since when?'

'A long time ago. And I was very happy when I found out.'

Discarded Souls

First came the sound of the earthquake that demolished the Berlin Wall, and then the tremors reached the walls of our prisons, bringing them down one by one.

The first to be released were prisoners who because of reconvictions had served more than the maximum provided for by the Criminal Code. Nuri was among them.

Within a few months we were all released.

Not long after, a group of foreigners knocked at my door, a Czech film crew that had arrived from Prague.

'One of your prison friends gave me your name,' said the director.

'Who?'

'Nuri Sallaku.'

'Why, where is Nuri?'

'In Prague.'

I immediately thought of Vlasta.

'But Vlasta must be married,' I said.

'Yes,' he replied, 'but still she asked Nuri to come to Prague, and he's working there now as a hospital doctor. Vlasta introduced him to a friend of hers, a widow. Nuri is living with her, but from what I can tell he and Vlasta are still very close, somehow beyond love.'

A short time later, he sent me the video of the documentary he had made. It was called *Studentska láska* (Student Love). It opened with a quotation from a speech by the dictator, which appeared in capital letters on the black screen:

'The modern revisionists and reactionaries call us Stalinists, and think this is an insult. In fact, it is an honour. To be a Stalinist means that the enemy has never defeated you, has never dishonoured you.'

Then Nuri and Vlasta appeared, now in their sixties, walking arm in arm on a Prague street, close by the bus route on which they had met.

Vlasta told the story from her point of view. At one point she showed the ring that Nuri had given her. But the ring was damaged. The green stone that Nuri had chosen as a symbol of hope was missing. She said that one day she found the stone gone. Amazingly this had happened at the very time when she received the message from Nuri, telling her to look to her own future.

Nuri at one point in the story produced a box that he opened with great care, and showed the white shoes he had bought for Vlasta. At the end he sang Solveig's song:

> *Spring and summer and autumn will pass*
> *And winter will cover the earth again.*
> *You will return, I will never forget you*
> *I gave you my heart in youth.*

I remembered what he had said many years previously: that Vlasta's love would be evidence that he would present to the devils, so they wouldn't throw him in the cauldron where they boil down the souls of people who depart this world leaving no trace behind. A prophecy fulfilled, I thought.

Perhaps out of a conviction or a need to believe that the future contains a promise of justice and compensation for suffering, I had at first closed this story with Solveig's song.

But one day in the course of the years that I spent writing these stories, a friend told me that Nuri had ended his life, throwing himself from a fifth-floor window of the hospital in Prague.

I thought back to the decision of the devils. Perhaps when he sang Solveig's aria to them, they told him they wouldn't put his soul in the pot. But when he decided to jump, it was because he heard them telling him to give himself up to the cauldron, because he wasn't worth keeping.

I also remembered Kujtim, in continual debate with devils in his poems over the future of his soul.

After Kujtim came out from prison, he spent most of his time writing down in notebooks the poems he'd stored in his mind. But soon his family noticed that he communicated with them less and less, and he was losing his memory. What happened to the poems he had remembered only he knew, but probably with the decay of his brain, these too vanished like footprints on a sandy beach.

His love poems from prison were not found written in his notebooks. Perhaps they disappeared with the last cells of his brain.

Then came a time when he began to use the ballpoint with which he was transcribing poems only to write the initials of his name and surname on the corner of his sheets, a prisoners' practice that he had followed for thirty-three years, so that his sheets wouldn't be mixed up in the laundry.

In the last week of his life, he developed a mania for hiding his personal belongings. This can only have been linked to his concealment of the implements of the murder he had committed in prison at the age of sixteen. Perhaps this was the deepest scar in his mind, the last memory that remained unquenched.

I don't think he had any conversation with the devils as he took these last steps.

* * *

When I try to understand why I chose to tell the stories of Nuri, Kujtim, and the others in this book, out of the thousands of human lives I encountered in prison, I have no single or clear answer.

I met these men and others when I joined that repellent whirlpool of prisoners, each of whom, like 'the caged wolf', was trying to escape being sucked in by that centripetal force. We were striving to break free into some kind of wide open space, where we would walk with body and soul at ease, with a meaning to life and death in our hearts.

At the start of this written journey through my memories of these lives, I thought that I had chosen them because they best illustrate the ambivalent feeling of the acceptance and refusal of a life spent thrown into this cauldron created by devils intentionally to destroy souls. As the years passed it became natural for us to see ourselves dressed in prison clothes, surrounded by that charred landscape, the barbed wire, and watchtowers, with the exhausting work in the mine, the enforced collective reading, roll-calls, and punishment cells. But few ever managed to consider these things as authentic parts of themselves. We all thought that on the day of our release our prison clothes would be left behind inside the perimeter fence with the watchtowers and barbed wire, and so our sole thought was to cast them aside for ever and return to our own clothes, our lives, and our true selves. But it becomes more difficult to think this way as I write about people like Kujtim, those who never managed to make any kind of life for themselves outside prison. Their wounds and the balm for these wounds, adaptation and resistance, became one and the same thing, their inner self. This raises the question of what was that true self we looked to find in this life outside prison, which we call freedom. At this point in the journey I think that I have written in order to accept them as my own, and to see these clothes, and these ordeals that I at first so determinedly refused, as belonging now to me, a part of my 'true' self, and realising that this wide open space where we will walk with body and soul at ease, with a meaning to life and death in our hearts, can only be found by taking stock of the shackles we have left behind.

FATOS LUBONJA is a leading figure in Albanian political life – both as a writer, a television commentator and a human rights activist. He is also the editor of the journal *Përpjekja/Endeavor*. At twenty-three, Lubonja was sentenced to seven years imprisonment for 'agitation and propaganda' after police found his diaries, which contained criticisms of Enver Hoxha. He was later resentenced and spent a total of 17 years in prison, much of it condemned to hard labour. He was released in 1991. Lubonja's first book in English, *Second Sentence: Inside the Albanian Gulag*, was published to great acclaim by I. B. Tauris in 2006, followed by *False Apocalypse: from Stalinism to Capitalism* (Istros, 2014). A number of his books or essays and articles have been translated into Italian, German, English, French, Polish, Japanese, Greek, Serbian. Among his many literary prizes, he received the Alberto Moravia Prize for International Literature in 2002 and the Herder Prize for Literature in 2004 and the Prince Claus Award, 2015.

JOHN HODGSON was born in England in 1951 and studied English at Cambridge and Newcastle. He has taught at the universities of Prishtina and Tirana and is the translator of Ismail Kadare's *Three-Arched Bridge* as well as many other novels by the same author. His translations have been lauded and awarded with numerous nominations for prizes over the years: he is the recipient of four English PEN Awards and his translation of Kadare's The Fall of the Stone City was shortlisted for The Independent Foreign Fiction Prize in 2013. John has written about Albania, Kosova, the British Balkan traveller Edith Durham, and the novelist John Cowper Powys. He has worked for the International Criminal Tribunal for the Former Yugoslavia in The Hague and now resides in London, working as an Albanian-English translator and interpreter. His previous title for Istros was Lubonja's *False Apocalypse*.

Lightning Source UK Ltd.
Milton Keynes UK
UKHW011146290822
407896UK00004B/487